M208 Pure

CW00546933

LA5

Eigenvectors

The Open University, Walton Hall, Milton Keynes, MK7 6AA.

First published 2006. Reprinted with amendments 2007.

Edited, designed and typeset by The Open University, using the Open University TeX System.

Printed and bound in the United Kingdom by Hobbs the Printers Limited, Brunel Road, Totton, Hampshire SO40 3WX.

ISBN 0 7492 0226 2

1.2

Contents

Introduction

By now you should be familiar with a wide variety of linear transformations from one vector space to another, and should appreciate that the matrix of a linear transformation depends on the bases chosen for the domain and codomain. Here we concentrate on linear transformations from $\mathbb{R}^2$ to $\mathbb{R}^2$, from $\mathbb{R}^3$ to $\mathbb{R}^3$ and, more generally, from $\mathbb{R}^n$ to $\mathbb{R}^n$.

Although we concentrate on linear transformations from $\mathbb{R}^n$ to $\mathbb{R}^n$, our results hold for linear transformations from any finite-dimensional vector space to itself.

For example, the linear transformation

$$t : \mathbb{R}^2 \longrightarrow \mathbb{R}^2$$
$$(x, y) \longmapsto (x + y, 2x + 3y)$$

has matrix

$$\mathbf{A} = \begin{pmatrix} 1 & 1 \\ 2 & 3 \end{pmatrix}$$

with respect to the standard basis $\{(1,0), (0,1)\}$ for both the domain and codomain, but has matrix

$$\mathbf{A} = \begin{pmatrix} -21 & -13 \\ 8 & 5 \end{pmatrix}$$

See Unit LA4, Exercise 2.9(c).

with respect to the non-standard bases $\{(1,2), (1,1)\}$ for the domain and $\{(1,0), (3,1)\}$ for the codomain.

We address the following question.

> Is it possible to find a basis for both the domain and codomain so that the matrix of a linear transformation is a diagonal matrix?

In the preceding units of this block, you have studied vectors, matrices, vector spaces and linear transformations. The method for finding a diagonal matrix of a linear transformation (if such a matrix exists) links all these topics together.

We begin Section 1 by looking at the images of lines under certain linear transformations from $\mathbb{R}^2$ to $\mathbb{R}^2$. We shall see that some lines through the origin are mapped to themselves by some of the linear transformations: the individual points on these invariant lines are usually moved, but, for a given line, all the points are scaled by a constant factor. Non-zero vectors on such a line are called *eigenvectors* and the constant scaling factor is the corresponding *eigenvalue*. Using determinants, we develop a method for finding the eigenvalues and eigenvectors of linear transformations from $\mathbb{R}^n$ to $\mathbb{R}^n$. We find that the set of eigenvectors corresponding to one eigenvalue, together with the zero vector, forms a subspace of $\mathbb{R}^n$. We call these subspaces *eigenspaces*.

In Section 2 we address the problem of finding a diagonal matrix associated with a given linear transformation. This problem is closely related to eigenvectors and eigenvalues. If there exists a basis consisting of eigenvectors of the linear transformation, then the matrix of the transformation, with respect to this basis for both the domain and codomain, is a diagonal matrix, whose diagonal entries are the eigenvalues of the transformation. Let $\mathbf{A}$ be the matrix of a linear transformation with respect to the standard basis for both the domain and codomain and let $\mathbf{D}$ be the matrix of the same linear transformation with respect to an eigenvector basis for both the domain and codomain.

We shall see that these matrices are related by the *transition matrix* $\mathbf{P}$ in the following way:

$$\mathbf{D} = \mathbf{P}^{-1}\mathbf{A}\mathbf{P}.$$

The columns of the transition matrix are formed from the eigenvectors in the basis.

Symmetric matrices are the topic of Section 3. We shall see that if the matrix of a linear transformation is *symmetric*, then a basis of eigenvectors can always be found. Therefore we can always find a diagonal matrix of such a linear transformation. Moreover, we can find an *orthonormal basis of eigenvectors*, consisting of basis vectors of unit length that are mutually orthogonal. The corresponding transition matrix $\mathbf{P}$ satisfies the additional property that $\mathbf{P}^{-1} = \mathbf{P}^T$. Such matrices are called *orthogonal matrices*.

In Section 4 we return to the study of non-degenerate conics. We use matrices and the techniques of Section 3 to write a given non-degenerate conic in standard form, and hence to classify it as an ellipse, a parabola or a hyperbola. We then look at *quadrics*, the three-dimensional analogues of conics, and use a similar method to write a given non-degenerate quadric in standard form and classify it as one of the six different types of non-degenerate quadric.

Unit LA1, Section 4.

Study guide

Sections 1–4 should be studied in the natural order.

It is important that you master the material in Section 1 fully before starting to study Section 2. After studying Sections 2 and 3, you should be able to diagonalise a given 2×2 or 3×3 matrix and orthogonally diagonalise a given symmetric 2×2 or 3×3 matrix.

1   Eigenvalues and eigenvectors

After working through this section, you should be able to:

(a) explain what are meant by the terms *eigenvalue*, *eigenvector*, *characteristic equation* and *eigenspace*;

(b) recognise the geometric interpretation of eigenvectors and eigenspaces in special cases;

(c) find the eigenvalues and eigenvectors of a given 2×2 or 3×3 matrix;

(d) describe some basic properties of eigenvalues and eigenvectors.

1.1   What is an eigenvector?

A linear transformation $t : \mathbb{R}^2 \longrightarrow \mathbb{R}^2$ moves the points of the plane around—fixing the origin, and mapping parallel lines to parallel lines. In this section we see that t may map some lines through the origin onto themselves. These 'unchanged' lines are rather special.

Consider the linear transformation $t : \mathbb{R}^2 \longrightarrow \mathbb{R}^2$ given by

$$t(x, y) = (x + 4y, x - 2y).$$

We know that t maps the origin $(0,0)$ to itself, since this is a property of all linear transformations.

We can calculate the image of the point $(1,0)$:

$$t(1,0) = (1 + (4 \times 0), 1 - (2 \times 0)) = (1,1).$$

Since linear transformations map lines through the origin to lines through the origin, t maps the line joining the points $(0,0)$ and $(1,0)$ to the line joining the points $(0,0)$ and $(1,1)$; that is,

t maps the line $y = 0$ to the line $y = x$.

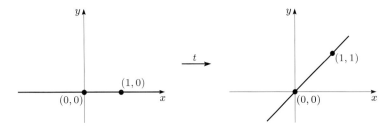

Let us now calculate the image of the point $(1,-1)$:

$$t(1,-1) = (1 + 4(-1), 1 - 2(-1)) = (-3,3).$$

In this case, the linear transformation t maps the line joining the points $(0,0)$ and $(1,-1)$ to the line joining the points $(0,0)$ and $(-3,3)$; that is,

t maps the line $y = -x$ to itself.

Although t moves individual points on the line (except $(0,0)$) to other points, the line *as a whole* is unchanged.

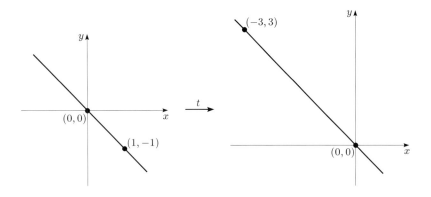

The image of the point $(1,-1)$ under t is the point $(-3,3) = -3(1,-1)$. The vector $(1,-1)$ is scaled (stretched) by a factor of -3; that is, the resulting vector is three times the original length and pointing in the opposite direction. In the next exercise we ask you to investigate how other vectors lying along the line $y = -x$ are moved by t.

Exercise 1.1   For the above linear transformation t, calculate the images of the vectors $(2,-2)$ and $(-7,7)$. What do you notice?

We have seen that the linear transformation t scales some vectors lying along the line $y = -x$ by the factor -3. This is true of any vector lying along this line, as we now show.

Let k be any real number, so that $(k,-k) = k(1,-1)$ is a vector lying along the line $y = -x$. Then

$$t(k,-k) = (k - 4k, k + 2k) = (-3k, 3k) = -3(k,-k),$$

so t has the same scaling effect on each vector $(k,-k)$ lying along the line $y = -x$.

Does the linear transformation t map other lines through the origin to themselves?

Exercise 1.2

(a) For the above linear transformation t, calculate $t(0,1)$, $t(1,2)$ and $t(4,1)$.

(b) Use one of the solutions to part (a) to write down another line in $\mathbb{R}^2$ that is mapped to itself by the linear transformation t.

(c) Find $t(4k, k)$.

We have seen that the linear transformation t maps each of the lines $y = -x$ and $x = 4y$ to itself. In both cases, each vector along the line is moved to a scalar multiple of itself: each vector lying along the line $y = -x$ is mapped to -3 times itself and each vector lying along the line $x = 4y$ is mapped to 2 times itself. We call the non-zero vectors lying along the line $y = -x$ *eigenvectors* of t with corresponding *eigenvalue* -3; for example, $(1, -1)$ and $(-7, 7)$ are eigenvectors of t with corresponding eigenvalue -3. Similarly, we call the non-zero vectors lying along the line $x = 4y$ eigenvectors of t with corresponding eigenvalue 2; for example, $(4, 1)$ and $(-8, -2)$ are eigenvectors of t with corresponding eigenvalue 2.

More generally, we make the following definitions; here and throughout this unit we use V to denote a finite-dimensional vector space.

Definitions   Let $t : V \longrightarrow V$ be a linear transformation. An **eigenvector** of t is a non-zero vector $\mathbf{v}$ that is mapped by t to a scalar multiple of itself; this scalar is the corresponding **eigenvalue**.

In symbols, a non-zero vector $\mathbf{v}$ is an eigenvector of a linear transformation t if

$$t(\mathbf{v}) = \lambda\mathbf{v}, \quad \text{for some } \lambda \in \mathbb{R};$$

λ is the corresponding eigenvalue.

Eigen is a German word meaning own, characteristic or special. Another name for eigenvalue is *characteristic value*.

Remark   We exclude the case $\mathbf{v} = \mathbf{0}$, since $t(\mathbf{0}) = \mathbf{0}$ for *every* linear transformation t.

It is, however, possible for λ to be 0; you will see an instance of this in Exercise 1.6.

In the example above we found two lines that are mapped to themselves by t, by considering the images of various points. This is a rather hit-and-miss way of finding eigenvalues and eigenvectors. Before developing a general method for finding them, we see that it is sometimes possible to do so by considering the geometry of the transformation.

Example 1.1   Let $t : \mathbb{R}^2 \longrightarrow \mathbb{R}^2$ be the linear transformation that maps each point to its reflection in the x-axis. By considering the geometric features of t, determine as many eigenvectors of t as you can and write down the corresponding eigenvalue in each case.

Solution   Reflection in the x-axis maps each point (x, y) to the point $(x, -y)$. It therefore maps each point on the x-axis to itself, since

$$t(k, 0) = (k, 0) = 1(k, 0),$$

so the vectors $(k, 0)$, with $k \neq 0$, are eigenvectors of t with corresponding eigenvalue 1. Note that $k \neq 0$, since we exclude the zero vector.

Similarly, each point on the y-axis is mapped to minus itself, since

$$t(0, k) = (0, -k) = -1(0, k),$$

so the vectors $(0, k)$, with $k \neq 0$, are eigenvectors of t with corresponding eigenvalue -1.

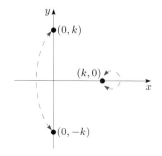

It is clear geometrically that every other line through the origin is changed by this transformation: we can find no other vector that maps to a multiple of itself. The only eigenvectors of t are therefore of the forms $(k, 0)$ with eigenvalue 1 and $(0, k)$ with eigenvalue -1, where $k \neq 0$. ∎

Exercise 1.3   By considering the geometric features of each of the following linear transformations of the plane, determine as many eigenvectors as you can and write down the corresponding eigenvalue in each case:

(a) reflection in the line $y = x$;

(b) 2-dilation;

(c) anticlockwise rotation through $\pi/2$ about the origin;

(d) anticlockwise rotation through π about the origin.

In Exercise 1.3 it is possible to spot the eigenvectors. We now illustrate a general method to determine the eigenvalues and eigenvectors for any given transformation.

Consider again the linear transformation $t : \mathbb{R}^2 \longrightarrow \mathbb{R}^2$ given by

$$t(x, y) = (x + 4y, x - 2y).$$

We wish to find those vectors (x, y) which are mapped to scalar multiples of themselves—that is,

$$t(x, y) = \lambda(x, y) = (\lambda x, \lambda y).$$

We equate the expressions for $t(x, y)$ and obtain

$$(x + 4y, x - 2y) = (\lambda x, \lambda y).$$

Comparing the first and second coordinates of these vectors, we obtain the simultaneous equations

$$\begin{cases} x + 4y = \lambda x, \\ x - 2y = \lambda y. \end{cases}$$

This is a system of two equations in the three unknowns x, y and λ. One way of solving this system is to move the terms on the right to the left-hand side. Thus we obtain the system

$$\begin{cases} (1 - \lambda)x + 4y = 0, \\ x + (-2 - \lambda)y = 0. \end{cases} \tag{1.1}$$

Equations (1.1) are called the *eigenvector equations*. We use them to find the possible values of λ, and then to find all the eigenvectors that correspond to these values. They are homogeneous equations in x and y.

Systems of homogeneous linear equations always have the trivial solution $x = 0$, $y = 0$, but this corresponds to the zero vector, which is excluded. Thus we seek *non-zero* solutions to the pair of homogeneous equations (1.1). Earlier, we saw that non-zero solutions exist if and only if the determinant of the coefficient matrix is 0; that is, if and only if

Unit LA2, Theorem 5.6, Summary Theorem.

$$\begin{vmatrix} 1 - \lambda & 4 \\ 1 & -2 - \lambda \end{vmatrix} = 0.$$

We expand this determinant and obtain

$$(1 - \lambda)(-2 - \lambda) - 4 = 0,$$

which simplifies (after some algebra) to

$$\lambda^2 + \lambda - 6 = 0.$$

This equation is called the *characteristic equation* of t, and its solutions are the eigenvalues we seek. In this case, we have

The characteristic equation is a polynomial equation in λ whose degree is the dimension of the domain of t—in this case, 2.

$$\lambda^2 + \lambda - 6 = (\lambda - 2)(\lambda + 3) = 0,$$

so the eigenvalues are $\lambda = 2$ and $\lambda = -3$.

To find the corresponding eigenvectors, we consider each eigenvalue λ in turn.

$\boxed{\lambda = 2}$ Putting $\lambda = 2$ into the eigenvector equations (1.1), we obtain

$$\begin{cases} -x + 4y = 0, \\ x - 4y = 0. \end{cases}$$

Notice that one equation is -1 times the other—the equations are equivalent to the single equation

$$x = 4y.$$

Thus the eigenvectors corresponding to $\lambda = 2$ are the non-zero vectors (x, y) for which $x = 4y$; that is, the vectors of the form

$$(4k, k), \quad \text{where } k \neq 0.$$

$\boxed{\lambda = -3}$ Putting $\lambda = -3$ into the eigenvector equations (1.1), we obtain

$$\begin{cases} 4x + 4y = 0, \\ x + y = 0. \end{cases}$$

These equations are equivalent to the single equation

$$y = -x.$$

Thus the eigenvectors corresponding to $\lambda = -3$ are the non-zero vectors (x, y) for which $y = -x$; that is, the vectors of the form

$$(k, -k), \quad \text{where } k \neq 0.$$

Thus the eigenvectors of t are the non-zero vectors of the forms

$$(4k, k), \text{ corresponding to } \lambda = 2,$$

and

$$(k, -k), \text{ corresponding to } \lambda = -3.$$

Note that this method produces *all* the eigenvalues and eigenvectors of the linear transformation.

Trying to show that these are the only ones by calculating the images of various points, as we did at the beginning of the section, would take forever!

Exercise 1.4   Let $t : \mathbb{R}^2 \longrightarrow \mathbb{R}^2$ be the linear transformation given by

$$t(x, y) = (-5x + 3y, 6x - 2y).$$

(a) Find the eigenvector equations of t.

(b) Find the characteristic equation of t, and solve it to find the eigenvalues of t.

(c) Solve the eigenvector equations, for each eigenvalue in turn, to find the eigenvectors of t.

1.2 Finding eigenvalues and eigenvectors

You have just seen how to find the eigenvalues and eigenvectors of a given linear transformation $t : \mathbb{R}^2 \longrightarrow \mathbb{R}^2$. This method, as it stands, is rather tedious to use to find eigenvalues and eigenvectors of linear transformations from $\mathbb{R}^3$ to $\mathbb{R}^3$, or $\mathbb{R}^4$ to $\mathbb{R}^4$, and so on. However, by introducing matrices, we can simplify the method.

We now work through the same example as in the previous subsection, but this time we introduce matrices.

With respect to the standard basis for $\mathbb{R}^2$, the linear transformation t given by $t(x, y) = (x + 4y, x - 2y)$ has the matrix representation

$$t : \mathbf{v} \longmapsto \mathbf{A}\mathbf{v}, \quad \text{where } \mathbf{v} = \begin{pmatrix} x \\ y \end{pmatrix} \text{ and } \mathbf{A} = \begin{pmatrix} 1 & 4 \\ 1 & -2 \end{pmatrix}.$$

Unit LA4, Section 2.

If $\mathbf{v}$ is an eigenvector of t with corresponding eigenvalue λ, then

$$t(\mathbf{v}) = \lambda\mathbf{v};$$

in matrix form, this becomes

$$\mathbf{A}\mathbf{v} = \lambda\mathbf{v},$$

that is,

$$\begin{pmatrix} 1 & 4 \\ 1 & -2 \end{pmatrix} \begin{pmatrix} x \\ y \end{pmatrix} = \lambda \begin{pmatrix} x \\ y \end{pmatrix}.$$

So

$$\begin{pmatrix} 1 & 4 \\ 1 & -2 \end{pmatrix} \begin{pmatrix} x \\ y \end{pmatrix} - \lambda \begin{pmatrix} x \\ y \end{pmatrix} = \begin{pmatrix} 0 \\ 0 \end{pmatrix}. \tag{1.2}$$

Note that

$$\lambda \begin{pmatrix} x \\ y \end{pmatrix} = \lambda \begin{pmatrix} 1 & 0 \\ 0 & 1 \end{pmatrix} \begin{pmatrix} x \\ y \end{pmatrix},$$

so equation (1.2) can be written as

$$\left[\begin{pmatrix} 1 & 4 \\ 1 & -2 \end{pmatrix} - \lambda \begin{pmatrix} 1 & 0 \\ 0 & 1 \end{pmatrix} \right] \begin{pmatrix} x \\ y \end{pmatrix} = \begin{pmatrix} 0 \\ 0 \end{pmatrix},$$

that is,

$$(\mathbf{A} - \lambda\mathbf{I})\mathbf{v} = \mathbf{0}.$$

We simplify this matrix equation and obtain

$$\begin{pmatrix} 1 - \lambda & 4 \\ 1 & -2 - \lambda \end{pmatrix} \begin{pmatrix} x \\ y \end{pmatrix} = \begin{pmatrix} 0 \\ 0 \end{pmatrix}.$$

Recall that

$$\mathbf{I} = \begin{pmatrix} 1 & 0 \\ 0 & 1 \end{pmatrix}$$

is the 2×2 identity matrix.

This gives rise to the eigenvector equations

$$\begin{cases} (1-\lambda)x + \qquad 4y = 0, \\ \qquad x + (-2-\lambda)y = 0, \end{cases}$$

as before. The characteristic equation is

$$\begin{vmatrix} 1-\lambda & 4 \\ 1 & -2-\lambda \end{vmatrix} = 0,$$

that is,

$$\det(\mathbf{A} - \lambda\mathbf{I}) = 0.$$

We can therefore find the characteristic equation directly from the matrix of the linear transformation (with respect to the standard basis for both the domain and codomain) by subtracting λ from each diagonal entry and then equating the determinant to zero.

Once we have found the eigenvalues, we use the same method as before to find the eigenvectors; that is, we substitute each eigenvalue in turn into the eigenvector equations and solve them.

In view of this connection with matrices, we adopt the following definitions.

See equations (1.1).

Definitions   A non-zero vector $\mathbf{v}$ is an **eigenvector** of a square matrix $\mathbf{A}$ if

$$\mathbf{A}\mathbf{v} = \lambda\mathbf{v}, \quad \text{for some } \lambda \in \mathbb{R};$$

λ is the corresponding **eigenvalue**.

The **characteristic equation** of a square matrix $\mathbf{A}$ is the equation

$$\det(\mathbf{A} - \lambda\mathbf{I}) = 0.$$

The matrix $\mathbf{A} - \lambda\mathbf{I}$ is obtained by subtracting λ from each entry on the diagonal of $\mathbf{A}$.

Remark   Eigenvalues and eigenvectors of matrices occur naturally in many applications—for example, in the study of vibrating mechanical systems. In such examples, the characteristic equation may have solutions that are not real numbers, and these *complex eigenvalues* have significance in these applications. In this unit, we are primarily interested in linear transformations of the plane and of three-dimensional space, so complex eigenvalues play no role here: we are concerned only with *real* eigenvalues and eigenvectors.

If a characteristic equation has no real solutions, then we say that there are no eigenvalues. For example, the matrix of the linear transformation representing an anticlockwise rotation through $\pi/2$ about the origin is

$$\mathbf{A} = \begin{pmatrix} 0 & -1 \\ 1 & 0 \end{pmatrix}.$$

See Exercise 1.3(c).

By the above definition, the characteristic equation of this linear transformation is

$$\det(\mathbf{A} - \lambda\mathbf{I}) = \begin{vmatrix} 0-\lambda & -1 \\ 1 & 0-\lambda \end{vmatrix} = 0.$$

We expand this determinant and obtain

$$\lambda^2 + 1 = 0.$$

This equation has no real solutions: the linear transformation has no eigenvalues and hence no eigenvectors. This agrees with the geometric interpretation—no line through the origin is mapped to itself by this rotation.

We summarise this matrix method for finding eigenvalues and eigenvectors in the following strategy.

Strategy 1.1   To determine the eigenvalues and eigenvectors of a square matrix $\mathbf{A}$.

1. Find the eigenvalues.

    Write down the characteristic equation

    $$\det(\mathbf{A} - \lambda \mathbf{I}) = 0.$$

    Expand this determinant to obtain a polynomial equation in λ.

    Solve this equation to find the eigenvalues.

2. Find the eigenvectors.

    Write down the eigenvector equations

    $$(\mathbf{A} - \lambda \mathbf{I})\mathbf{v} = \mathbf{0}.$$

    For each eigenvalue λ, solve this system of linear equations to find the corresponding eigenvectors.

We illustrate Strategy 1.1 with the following example.

Example 1.2   Let $t : \mathbb{R}^2 \longrightarrow \mathbb{R}^2$ be the linear transformation given by

$$t(x, y) = (5x + 2y, 2x + 5y).$$

Write down the matrix of t with respect to the standard basis for $\mathbb{R}^2$, and find the eigenvalues and eigenvectors of t.

Solution   The matrix of t with respect to the standard basis for $\mathbb{R}^2$ is

$$\mathbf{A} = \begin{pmatrix} 5 & 2 \\ 2 & 5 \end{pmatrix}.$$

We use Strategy 1.1 to find the eigenvalues and eigenvectors of $\mathbf{A}$, which are the same as those of t.

First we find the eigenvalues of $\mathbf{A}$.

The characteristic equation of $\mathbf{A}$ is $\det(\mathbf{A} - \lambda \mathbf{I}) = 0$; that is,

$$\begin{vmatrix} 5 - \lambda & 2 \\ 2 & 5 - \lambda \end{vmatrix} = 0.$$

We expand this determinant and obtain

$$(5 - \lambda)^2 - 4 = 0,$$

which simplifies to

$$\lambda^2 - 10\lambda + 21 = (\lambda - 7)(\lambda - 3) = 0.$$

The eigenvalues of $\mathbf{A}$ are therefore $\lambda = 7$ and $\lambda = 3$.

Next we find the eigenvectors of $\mathbf{A}$.

The eigenvector equations are

$$\begin{cases} (5 - \lambda)x + 2y = 0, \\ 2x + (5 - \lambda)y = 0. \end{cases}$$

$\boxed{\lambda = 7}$ The eigenvector equations become

$$\begin{cases} -2x + 2y = 0, \\ 2x - 2y = 0. \end{cases}$$

These equations are equivalent to the single equation

$$y = x.$$

Thus the eigenvectors corresponding to $\lambda = 7$ are the non-zero vectors for which $y = x$; that is, the vectors of the form

$$(k, k), \quad \text{where } k \neq 0.$$

$\boxed{\lambda = 3}$ The eigenvector equations become

$$\begin{cases} 2x + 2y = 0, \\ 2x + 2y = 0. \end{cases}$$

These equations are equivalent to the single equation

$$y = -x.$$

Thus the eigenvectors corresponding to $\lambda = 3$ are the non-zero vectors for which $y = -x$; that is, the vectors of the form

$$(k, -k), \quad \text{where } k \neq 0.$$

Thus the eigenvectors of the linear transformation t are the non-zero vectors of the forms

$$(k, k), \text{ corresponding to } \lambda = 7,$$

and

$$(k, -k), \text{ corresponding to } \lambda = 3. \quad \blacksquare$$

Exercise 1.5   For each of the following linear transformations $t : \mathbb{R}^2 \longrightarrow \mathbb{R}^2$, write down the matrix of t with respect to the standard basis for $\mathbb{R}^2$, and find the eigenvalues and eigenvectors of t.

(a) $t(x, y) = (x + 3y, 2x - 4y)$ (b) $t(x, y) = (x - 2y, -2x - 2y)$

So far, we have concentrated on linear transformations from $\mathbb{R}^2$ to $\mathbb{R}^2$ and on 2×2 matrices. We now use Strategy 1.1 to find the eigenvalues and eigenvectors of a linear transformation from $\mathbb{R}^3$ to $\mathbb{R}^3$ using a 3×3 matrix.

Example 1.3   Let $t : \mathbb{R}^3 \longrightarrow \mathbb{R}^3$ be the linear transformation given by

$$t(x, y, z) = (2x + z, -x + 2y + 3z, x + 2z).$$

Write down the matrix of t with respect to the standard basis for $\mathbb{R}^3$, and find the eigenvalues and eigenvectors of t.

Solution   The matrix of t with respect to the standard basis for $\mathbb{R}^3$ is

$$\mathbf{A} - \begin{pmatrix} 2 & 0 & 1 \\ -1 & 2 & 3 \\ 1 & 0 & 2 \end{pmatrix}.$$

We use Strategy 1.1 to find the eigenvalues and eigenvectors of $\mathbf{A}$, which are the same as those of t.

First we find the eigenvalues of $\mathbf{A}$.

The characteristic equation is $\det(\mathbf{A} - \lambda \mathbf{I}) = 0$; that is,

Here $\mathbf{I}$ is the 3×3 identity matrix.

$$\begin{vmatrix} 2 - \lambda & 0 & 1 \\ -1 & 2 - \lambda & 3 \\ 1 & 0 & 2 - \lambda \end{vmatrix} = 0.$$

We expand this determinant, and obtain

$$(2 - \lambda)\begin{vmatrix} 2 - \lambda & 3 \\ 0 & 2 - \lambda \end{vmatrix} - 0 + \begin{vmatrix} -1 & 2 - \lambda \\ 1 & 0 \end{vmatrix} = 0.$$

Simplifying this expression, we obtain

$$(2 - \lambda)((2 - \lambda)^2 - 0) + (0 - (2 - \lambda)) = 0,$$

so $(2 - \lambda)[(2 - \lambda)^2 - 1] = 0,$

or $(2 - \lambda)(\lambda^2 - 4\lambda + 3) = 0.$

When there is a common factor, such as $2 - \lambda$, it is best to keep this separate—the problem then reduces to factorising the remaining quadratic polynomial.

We can factorise this characteristic equation as

$$(2 - \lambda)(\lambda - 3)(\lambda - 1) = 0.$$

The eigenvalues of **A** are therefore $\lambda = 3$, $\lambda = 2$ and $\lambda = 1$.

Next we find the eigenvectors of **A**.

The eigenvector equations are

$$\begin{cases} (2 - \lambda)x & + & z = 0, \\ -x + (2 - \lambda)y + & 3z = 0, \\ x & + (2 - \lambda)z = 0. \end{cases}$$

$\boxed{\lambda = 3}$ The eigenvector equations become

$$\begin{cases} -x & + & z = 0, \\ -x - y + 3z = 0, \\ x & - & z = 0. \end{cases}$$

When solving the eigenvector equations for matrices of size 3×3 and larger, it is sometimes necessary to use the method of Gauss–Jordan elimination from Unit LA2. In worked examples here, we do not use this method as the solutions can be found directly.

The first and third equations imply that

$$z = x.$$

Substituting this into the second equation, we obtain

$$2x - y = 0.$$

Thus the eigenvectors corresponding to $\lambda = 3$ are the non-zero vectors (x, y, z) satisfying $z = x$ and $y = 2x$; that is, the vectors of the form

$$(k, 2k, k), \quad \text{where } k \neq 0.$$

$\boxed{\lambda = 2}$ The eigenvector equations become

$$\begin{cases} & z = 0, \\ -x & + 3z = 0, \\ x & = 0. \end{cases}$$

These equations have the solution

$$z = 0 \quad \text{and} \quad x = 0.$$

However, there are no constraints on the unknown y. Thus the eigenvectors corresponding to $\lambda = 2$ are the non-zero vectors (x, y, z) satisfying $x = 0$ and $z = 0$; that is, the vectors of the form

$$(0, k, 0), \quad \text{where } k \neq 0.$$

$\boxed{\lambda = 1}$ The eigenvector equations become

$$\begin{cases} x & + & z = 0, \\ -x + y + 3z = 0, \\ x & + & z = 0. \end{cases}$$

The first and third equations imply that

$$z = -x.$$

Substituting this into the second equation yields the equation

$$-4x + y = 0.$$

Thus the eigenvectors corresponding to $\lambda = 1$ are the non-zero vectors (x, y, z) satisfying $z = -x$ and $y = 4x$; that is, the vectors of the form

$$(k, 4k, -k), \quad \text{where } k \neq 0.$$

Thus the eigenvectors of the linear transformation t are the non-zero vectors of the forms

$$(k, 2k, k), \text{ corresponding to } \lambda = 3,$$
$$(0, k, 0), \text{ corresponding to } \lambda = 2,$$

and

$$(k, 4k, -k), \text{ corresponding to } \lambda = 1. \quad \blacksquare$$

There are two points to note here. The first point is that a cubic polynomial may not be easy to factorise. We shall usually deal with examples that factorise easily.

You studied ways of factorising polynomials in the Unit I2.

The second point is that there is a useful check on the values found for the eigenvalues—*the sum of the eigenvalues should be equal to the sum of the diagonal entries of the matrix* $\mathbf{A}$. In Example 1.3 the eigenvalues are 3, 2 and 1, which sum to 6, and the diagonal entries of the matrix $\mathbf{A}$ are 2, 2 and 2, which also sum to 6.

The sum of the diagonal entries of a matrix is called the trace of the matrix.

> **Exercise 1.6**   Let $t : \mathbb{R}^3 \longrightarrow \mathbb{R}^3$ be the linear transformation given by
>
> $$t(x, y, z) = (4x + 2y, 2x + 3y + 2z, 2y + 2z).$$
>
> Write down the matrix of t with respect to the standard basis for $\mathbb{R}^3$, and find the eigenvalues and eigenvectors of t.

In most of the examples we have seen so far, the eigenvalues have not been easy to recognise directly and Strategy 1.1 has been required to find them. This is not always the case, as the following exercise illustrates.

> **Exercise 1.7**   Find the eigenvalues of each of the following matrices.
>
> (a) $\begin{pmatrix} 1 & 2 \\ 0 & 6 \end{pmatrix}$ (b) $\begin{pmatrix} 8 & 0 & 0 \\ 0 & -5 & 0 \\ 0 & 0 & 21 \end{pmatrix}$ (c) $\begin{pmatrix} 4 & 0 & 0 \\ 25 & -2 & 0 \\ 17 & \pi & 6 \end{pmatrix}$

Finding eigenvalues of triangular and diagonal matrices is straightforward, as Exercise 1.7 illustrates. The eigenvalues are the diagonal entries of the matrix and no calculation is needed to find them.

> **Theorem 1.1**   The eigenvalues of a triangular matrix and of a diagonal matrix are the diagonal entries of the matrix.

The proofs are straightforward, but we omit them for reasons of space.

1.3 Eigenspaces

In Subsection 1.1 we considered the linear transformation $t : \mathbb{R}^2 \longrightarrow \mathbb{R}^2$ given by

$$t(x, y) = (x + 4y, x - 2y),$$

and saw that each of the lines $y = -x$ and $x = 4y$ is mapped to itself.

The line $y = -x$ consists of the points of the form $(k, -k)$, each of which is an eigenvector of t corresponding to the eigenvalue $\lambda = -3$, except when $k = 0$, which is specifically excluded.

Similarly, the line $x = 4y$ consists of the points of the form $(4k, k)$, each of which is an eigenvector corresponding to the eigenvalue $\lambda = 2$, except when $k = 0$.

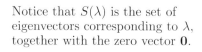

For each eigenvalue λ, if we look at *all* the solutions to the equation $t(\mathbf{v}) = \lambda\mathbf{v}$ (including $\mathbf{0}$), then we obtain a line through the origin. The set of such solutions is a subspace of the domain of t.

Theorem 1.2   Let $t : V \longrightarrow V$ be a linear transformation. For each eigenvalue λ of t, let $S(\lambda)$ be the set of vectors satisfying $t(\mathbf{v}) = \lambda\mathbf{v}$. Then $S(\lambda)$ is a subspace of V.

Notice that $S(\lambda)$ is the set of eigenvectors corresponding to λ, together with the zero vector $\mathbf{0}$.

Proof   Consider any eigenvalue λ of a linear transformation $t : V \longrightarrow V$. Following Unit LA3, Strategy 4.1, first we check that $\mathbf{0} \in S(\lambda)$. This follows since, for any linear transformation t,

$t(\mathbf{0}) = \mathbf{0} = \lambda\mathbf{0}$.

Next we check that if $\mathbf{v}_1, \mathbf{v}_2 \in S(\lambda)$, then $\mathbf{v}_1 + \mathbf{v}_2 \in S(\lambda)$.

Now, $t(\mathbf{v}_1 + \mathbf{v}_2) = t(\mathbf{v}_1) + t(\mathbf{v}_2) = \lambda\mathbf{v}_1 + \lambda\mathbf{v}_2 = \lambda(\mathbf{v}_1 + \mathbf{v}_2)$.

Thus $\mathbf{v}_1 + \mathbf{v}_2 \in S(\lambda)$.

Finally, we check that if $\mathbf{v} \in S(\lambda)$ and $\alpha \in \mathbb{R}$, then $\alpha\mathbf{v} \in S(\lambda)$.

Now, $t(\alpha\mathbf{v}) = \alpha\, t(\mathbf{v}) = \alpha\lambda\mathbf{v} = \lambda(\alpha\mathbf{v})$.

Thus $\alpha\mathbf{v} \in S(\lambda)$.

The conditions are satisfied, so $S(\lambda)$ is a subspace of V.   ∎

Since $S(\lambda)$ is a subspace mainly comprising eigenvectors, we call it an *eigenspace*.

Definition   Let $t : V \longrightarrow V$ be a linear transformation and, for each eigenvalue λ of t, let $S(\lambda)$ be the set of vectors satisfying $t(\mathbf{v}) = \lambda\mathbf{v}$. Then $S(\lambda)$ is the **eigenspace** of t corresponding to the eigenvalue λ.

Example 1.4   Let $t : \mathbb{R}^3 \longrightarrow \mathbb{R}^3$ be the linear transformation given by

$t(x, y, z) = (4x + 2y, 2x + 3y + 2z, 2y + 2z)$.

Find the eigenspace $S(0)$ of t, specify a basis for it and state its dimension.

Solution   The non-zero vectors of the form $(k, -2k, 2k)$ are the eigenvectors of t corresponding to the eigenvalue $\lambda = 0$.

You found the eigenvalues and eigenvectors of this linear transformation in Exercise 1.6.

The eigenspace $S(0)$ is therefore the set of vectors

$\{(k, -2k, 2k) : k \in \mathbb{R}\}$.

Any vector in $S(0)$ can be written as $k(1, -2, 2)$, so

$\{(1, -2, 2)\}$

is a basis for $S(0)$. Thus $S(0)$ has dimension 1.

Geometrically, $S(0)$ is a line through the origin in the direction of the vector $(1, -2, 2)$.   ∎

Exercise 1.8   For the linear transformation t in Example 1.4, find the eigenspaces $S(6)$ and $S(3)$. In each case, specify a basis and state the dimension of the eigenspace.

The eigenvectors of t are the non-zero vectors of the forms $(2k, 2k, k)$, corresponding to $\lambda = 6$, and $(-2k, k, 2k)$, corresponding to $\lambda = 3$.

Example 1.5   Let $t : \mathbb{R}^3 \longrightarrow \mathbb{R}^3$ be the linear transformation given by

$$t(x, y, z) = (0, y, z).$$

Find all the eigenspaces of t. In each case, specify a basis and state the dimension of the eigenspace.

Solution   The matrix of t with respect to the standard basis for $\mathbb{R}^3$ is

$$\mathbf{A} = \begin{pmatrix} 0 & 0 & 0 \\ 0 & 1 & 0 \\ 0 & 0 & 1 \end{pmatrix}.$$

This matrix is diagonal, so the eigenvalues are the diagonal entries: $\lambda = 0$, $\lambda = 1$ and $\lambda = 1$.

The eigenvector equations are

$$\begin{cases} -\lambda x & = 0, \\ (1 - \lambda)y & = 0, \\ (1 - \lambda)z = 0. \end{cases}$$

$\boxed{\lambda = 0}$ The eigenvector equations become $0x = 0$, $y = 0$ and $z = 0$. Thus the eigenvectors corresponding to the eigenvalue $\lambda = 0$ are the non-zero vectors (x, y, z) satisfying $y = 0$ and $z = 0$; that is, the vectors of the form

$$(k, 0, 0), \quad \text{where } k \neq 0.$$

The eigenspace $S(0)$ is the set of vectors

$$\{(k, 0, 0) : k \in \mathbb{R}\}.$$

Any vector in $S(0)$ can be written as $k(1, 0, 0)$, so

$$\{(1, 0, 0)\}$$

is a basis for $S(0)$. Thus $S(0)$ has dimension 1.

Geometrically, $S(0)$ is the x-axis in $\mathbb{R}^3$.

$\boxed{\lambda = 1}$ The eigenvector equations reduce to the single equation

$$-x = 0.$$

Thus the eigenvectors corresponding to the eigenvalue $\lambda = 1$ are the non-zero vectors (x, y, z) satisfying $x = 0$; that is, the vectors of the form

$$(0, k, l), \quad \text{where } k \text{ and } l \text{ are not both } 0.$$

The eigenspace $S(1)$ is the set of vectors

$$\{(0, k, l) : k, l \in \mathbb{R}\}.$$

Any vector in $S(1)$ can be written as $k(0, 1, 0) + l(0, 0, 1)$, so

$$\{(0, 1, 0), (0, 0, 1)\}$$

is a basis for $S(1)$. Thus $S(1)$ has dimension 2.

Geometrically, $S(1)$ is the plane through the origin given by $x = 0$.   ∎

In Example 1.5 the (simplified) characteristic equation of the linear transformation t is

$$\lambda(\lambda - 1)^2 = 0.$$

The eigenvalue $\lambda = 1$ is a *multiple root* of this characteristic equation; we say that $\lambda = 1$ has *multiplicity* 2 because the factor $(\lambda - 1)$ occurs twice.

In general, we adopt the following definition.

Definition   If the characteristic equation of a square matrix $\mathbf{A}$ can be written as

$$(\lambda - \lambda_1)^{m_1}(\lambda - \lambda_2)^{m_2} \ldots (\lambda - \lambda_p)^{m_p} = 0,$$

where $\lambda_1, \lambda_2, \ldots, \lambda_p$ are distinct, then the eigenvalue λ_j of $\mathbf{A}$ has **multiplicity** m_j, for $j = 1, 2, \ldots, p$.

Exercise 1.9   (Harder)   Find the eigenvalues and eigenvectors of the matrix

$$\begin{pmatrix} 4 & 2 & 2 \\ 2 & 4 & 2 \\ 2 & 2 & 4 \end{pmatrix}.$$

For each eigenvalue λ, state its multiplicity, find the corresponding eigenspace $S(\lambda)$, specify a basis for $S(\lambda)$ and state its dimension.

Hint: It may help you to factorise the characteristic equation, to know that one of the eigenvalues is 8.

From the examples that you have seen so far, you may be tempted to conjecture that the dimension of the eigenspace $S(\lambda)$, for a given eigenvalue λ, is equal to the multiplicity of λ. The following exercise gives you the chance to investigate this conjecture.

Exercise 1.10   Find the eigenvalues and eigenvectors of the matrix

$$\begin{pmatrix} 1 & 1 \\ 0 & 1 \end{pmatrix}.$$

For each eigenvalue λ, state its multiplicity, find the corresponding eigenspace $S(\lambda)$, specify a basis for $S(\lambda)$ and state its dimension.

In Exercise 1.10 the eigenvalue $\lambda = 1$ has multiplicity 2, but it gives rise to an eigenspace of dimension only 1. In this case, the matrix represents a shear and the only line through the origin left unchanged is the x-axis. Thus there is a single one-dimensional eigenspace, so the conjecture is false.

In general, it can be shown that the dimension of an eigenspace cannot exceed the multiplicity of the corresponding eigenvalue, but we shall not do this.

Further exercises

Exercise 1.11   Let $\mathbf{v}$ be an eigenvector of a linear transformation t with corresponding eigenvalue λ. Prove that if $k \neq 0$, then $k\mathbf{v}$ is also an eigenvector of t with corresponding eigenvalue λ.

Exercise 1.12   Let $t : \mathbb{R}^2 \longrightarrow \mathbb{R}^2$ be the linear transformation given by

$$t(x, y) = (-5x + 3y, 6x - 2y).$$

Find the eigenvalues and eigenvectors of t.

Exercise 1.13   Let $t : \mathbb{R}^3 \longrightarrow \mathbb{R}^3$ be the linear transformation given by

$$t(x, y, z) = (3x + 2y + 2z, -2x - 2y - 2z, x + 2y + 2z).$$

Find the eigenvalues and eigenvectors of t.

Exercise 1.14   Let $\mathbf{A} = \begin{pmatrix} a & b \\ c & d \end{pmatrix}$.

Find the characteristic equation of $\mathbf{A}$.

Show that the sum of the eigenvalues is equal to $a + d$; that is, the sum of the diagonal entries of $\mathbf{A}$.

Hint: Use the formula for finding the solutions to a quadratic equation.

Exercise 1.15   Let $t : \mathbb{R}^3 \longrightarrow \mathbb{R}^3$ be the linear transformation given by

$$t(x, y, z) = (-2z, x + 2y + z, x + 3z).$$

Find all the eigenspaces of t. For each one, specify a basis and state the dimension of the eigenspace.

2   Diagonalising matrices

After working through this section, you should be able to:

(a) write down the matrix of a linear transformation t with respect to a given eigenvector basis of t;

(b) write down the *transition matrix* from an eigenvector basis to the standard basis;

(c) *diagonalise* a given square matrix, if possible.

2.1 Eigenvector bases

In Section 1 we introduced the notions of an eigenvalue λ and corresponding eigenvector $\mathbf{v}$ of a linear transformation $t : \mathbb{R}^n \longrightarrow \mathbb{R}^n$; that is, a non-zero vector $\mathbf{v}$ whose image $t(\mathbf{v})$ is $\lambda \mathbf{v}$. For example, in Exercise 1.5(a) you saw that the linear transformation $t : \mathbb{R}^2 \longrightarrow \mathbb{R}^2$ given by

$$t(x, y) = (x + 3y, 2x - 4y)$$

has eigenvalues $\lambda = -5$ and $\lambda = 2$ with corresponding eigenvectors $(1, \ 2)$ and $(3, 1)$. Since $(3, 1)$ is not a multiple of $(1, -2)$, these two eigenvectors are linearly independent, so they form a basis for $\mathbb{R}^2$—the domain and codomain of t. We say that $\{(1, -2), (3, 1)\}$ is an *eigenvector basis* of t.

Definition   Let $t : \mathbb{R}^n \longrightarrow \mathbb{R}^n$ be a linear transformation and let E be a basis for $\mathbb{R}^n$ consisting of eigenvectors of t. The basis E is an **eigenvector basis** of t.

Exercise 2.1   Verify that $\{(-2, 1), (1, 2)\}$ is an eigenvector basis of the linear transformation $t : \mathbb{R}^2 \longrightarrow \mathbb{R}^2$ given by

$$t(x, y) = (x - 2y, -2x - 2y).$$

Use the solution to Exercise 1.5(b).

19

Exercise 2.2   The set $E = \{(0, 1, -1), (-2, 1, 0), (1, 0, -1)\}$ is a basis for $\mathbb{R}^3$. Verify that E is an eigenvector basis of the linear transformation $t : \mathbb{R}^3 \longrightarrow \mathbb{R}^3$ given by

$$t(x, y, z) = (-x + 2y + 2z, 2x + 2y + 2z, -3x - 6y - 6z).$$

In the previous unit we gave a strategy (Strategy 2.1) for finding the matrix representation of a linear transformation $t : V \longrightarrow W$ with respect to given bases E and F for the domain and codomain of t. In this section you will see that this matrix representation is particularly simple if $W = V$, E is an eigenvector basis of t and $F = E$. We begin by reminding you of the strategy in the particular case when $W = V$ and $F = E$.

Unit LA4, Subsection 2.1.

Strategy 2.1   To find the matrix $\mathbf{A}$ of a linear transformation $t : V \longrightarrow V$ with respect to the basis $E = \{\mathbf{e}_1, \mathbf{e}_2, \ldots, \mathbf{e}_n\}$.

1.   Find the images $t(\mathbf{e}_1), t(\mathbf{e}_2), \ldots, t(\mathbf{e}_n)$.

2.   Find the E-coordinates of the image vectors from step 1.

3.   For each $j = 1, 2, \ldots, n$, use the E-coordinates of $t(\mathbf{e}_j)$ to form column j of the matrix $\mathbf{A}$.

Recall that if $E = \{\mathbf{e}_1, \mathbf{e}_2, \ldots, \mathbf{e}_n\}$ is a basis for V, and $\mathbf{v}$ is a vector in V such that $\mathbf{v} = v_1\mathbf{e}_1 + \cdots + v_n\mathbf{e}_n$, then the numbers $v_1, \ldots, v_n$ are the E-coordinates of $\mathbf{v}$, and $\mathbf{v}_E = (v_1, \ldots, v_n)_E$ is the E-coordinate representation of $\mathbf{v}$. If E is the standard basis for V, then we usually omit the suffix E.

In the next example, we illustrate what happens when we find the matrix of a linear transformation t with respect to an eigenvector basis of t.

Example 2.1   Consider the linear transformation $t : \mathbb{R}^2 \longrightarrow \mathbb{R}^2$ given by

$$t(x, y) = (x + 3y, 2x - 4y).$$

(a) Write down the matrix of t with respect to the standard basis for $\mathbb{R}^2$.

(b) Find the matrix of t with respect to the eigenvector basis

$$E = \{(1, -2), (3, 1)\}.$$

Solution

(a) The matrix of t with respect to the standard basis for $\mathbb{R}^2$ is

$$\begin{pmatrix} 1 & 3 \\ 2 & -4 \end{pmatrix}.$$

(b) Following Strategy 2.1, first we find the images of the vectors in the basis $E = \{(1, -2), (3, 1)\}$:

$$t(1, -2) = (-5, 10) \quad \text{and} \quad t(3, 1) = (6, 2).$$

Next we find the E-coordinates of each of these image vectors:

$$t(1, -2) = (-5, 10) = -5(1, -2) + 0(3, 1) = (-5, 0)_E,$$
$$t(3, 1) = (6, 2) = 0(1, -2) + 2(3, 1) = (0, 2)_E.$$

So the matrix of t with respect to the eigenvector basis E is

$$\begin{pmatrix} -5 & 0 \\ 0 & 2 \end{pmatrix}. \quad \blacksquare$$

In Example 2.1(b) we found that the matrix of t with respect to the eigenvector basis is diagonal and that its diagonal entries are the eigenvalues of the linear transformation t. You should find a similar outcome in the next exercise.

Exercise 2.3 Consider the linear transformation $t : \mathbb{R}^2 \longrightarrow \mathbb{R}^2$ given by

$$t(x, y) = (x - 2y, -2x - 2y).$$

(a) Write down the matrix of t with respect to the standard basis for $\mathbb{R}^2$.

(b) Find the matrix of t with respect to the eigenvector basis

$$E = \{(-2, 1), (1, 2)\}.$$

Example 2.1(b) and Exercise 2.3(b) are special cases of the following result.

Theorem 2.1 Let $t : \mathbb{R}^n \longrightarrow \mathbb{R}^n$ be a linear transformation, let $E = \{\mathbf{e}_1, \mathbf{e}_2, \ldots, \mathbf{e}_n\}$ be an eigenvector basis of t and let $t(\mathbf{e}_j) = \lambda_j \mathbf{e}_j$, for $j = 1, 2, \ldots, n$. Then the matrix of t with respect to the eigenvector basis E is

$$\mathbf{D} = \begin{pmatrix} \lambda_1 & 0 & \cdots & 0 \\ 0 & \lambda_2 & \cdots & 0 \\ \vdots & \vdots & & \vdots \\ 0 & 0 & \cdots & \lambda_n \end{pmatrix}.$$

We use the letter $\mathbf{D}$ because the matrix is diagonal.

Proof   Let t and E be as in the statement of the theorem. We use Strategy 2.1 to find the matrix of t with respect to the eigenvector basis E.

We know that

$$t(\mathbf{e}_j) = \lambda_j \mathbf{e}_j, \quad \text{for } j = 1, 2, \ldots, n.$$

Next we find the E-coordinates of each of these image vectors:

$$t(\mathbf{e}_1) = \lambda_1 \mathbf{e}_1 + 0\mathbf{e}_2 + \cdots + 0\mathbf{e}_n = (\lambda_1, 0, \ldots, 0)_E,$$
$$t(\mathbf{e}_2) = 0\mathbf{e}_1 + \lambda_2 \mathbf{e}_2 + \cdots + 0\mathbf{e}_n = (0, \lambda_2, \ldots, 0)_E,$$
$$\vdots$$
$$t(\mathbf{e}_n) = 0\mathbf{e}_1 + 0\mathbf{e}_2 + \cdots + \lambda_n \mathbf{e}_n = (0, 0, \ldots, \lambda_n)_E.$$

So the matrix of t with respect to the eigenvector basis E is

$$\mathbf{D} = \begin{pmatrix} \lambda_1 & 0 & \cdots & 0 \\ 0 & \lambda_2 & \cdots & 0 \\ \vdots & \vdots & & \vdots \\ 0 & 0 & \cdots & \lambda_n \end{pmatrix},$$

as claimed. ∎

Exercise 2.4 Consider the linear transformation $t : \mathbb{R}^3 \longrightarrow \mathbb{R}^3$ given by

$$t(x, y, z) = (-x + 2y + 2z, 2x + 2y + 2z, -3x - 6y - 6z).$$

Use the solution to Exercise 2.2 to write down the matrix of t with respect to the eigenvector basis

$$E = \{(0, 1, -1), (-2, 1, 0), (1, 0, -1)\}.$$

2.2 Transition matrices

Suppose that $t : \mathbb{R}^n \longrightarrow \mathbb{R}^n$ is a linear transformation and E is an eigenvector basis of t. We have just shown that the matrix of t with respect to the eigenvector basis E is a diagonal matrix $\mathbf{D}$.

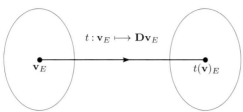

Eigenvector basis E for domain and codomain

It is natural to ask whether there is any relationship between this matrix $\mathbf{D}$ and the matrix $\mathbf{A}$ of t with respect to the standard basis for $\mathbb{R}^n$.

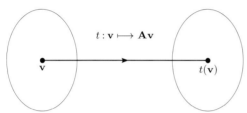

Standard basis for domain and codomain

We now show that there is an algebraic relationship between the matrices $\mathbf{D}$ and $\mathbf{A}$. To do this, first we find an algebraic relationship between the E-coordinate representation $\mathbf{v}_E$ and the standard coordinate representation. We begin by doing this for the example that we considered at the beginning of the section, where $t : \mathbb{R}^2 \longrightarrow \mathbb{R}^2$ is the linear transformation given by

$$t(x, y) = (x + 3y, 2x - 4y)$$

and E is the eigenvector basis $\{(1, -2), (3, 1)\}$.

Suppose that the E-coordinate representation of a vector $\mathbf{v}$ in $\mathbb{R}^2$ is

$$\mathbf{v}_E = (a, b)_E.$$

What are the standard coordinates of $\mathbf{v}$?

In column form,

$$\mathbf{v} = a \begin{pmatrix} 1 \\ -2 \end{pmatrix} + b \begin{pmatrix} 3 \\ 1 \end{pmatrix} = \begin{pmatrix} a + 3b \\ -2a + b \end{pmatrix} = \begin{pmatrix} 1 & 3 \\ -2 & 1 \end{pmatrix} \begin{pmatrix} a \\ b \end{pmatrix}_E.$$

Thus

$$\mathbf{v} = \mathbf{P}\mathbf{v}_E,$$

where

$$\mathbf{P} = \begin{pmatrix} 1 & 3 \\ -2 & 1 \end{pmatrix}.$$

Notice that $\det \mathbf{P} = 1 - (-6) = 7 \neq 0$, so $\mathbf{P}$ is invertible. Since $\mathbf{v} = \mathbf{P}\mathbf{v}_E$, it follows that

$$\mathbf{P}^{-1}\mathbf{v} = \mathbf{P}^{-1}(\mathbf{P}\mathbf{v}_E) = (\mathbf{P}^{-1}\mathbf{P})\mathbf{v}_E = \mathbf{v}_E.$$

So premultiplication by the matrix $\mathbf{P}$ converts the E-coordinate representation of a vector into the standard coordinate representation and, similarly, premultiplication by the matrix $\mathbf{P}^{-1}$ converts the standard coordinate representation of a vector into the E-coordinate representation.

Note that there is a simple relationship between the matrix $\mathbf{P}$ and the eigenvector basis E—the columns of $\mathbf{P}$ are formed from the standard coordinates of the vectors in E. We call $\mathbf{P}$ the *transition matrix* from the basis E to the standard basis for $\mathbb{R}^2$.

The general definition is as follows.

Definition   Let $E = \{\mathbf{e}_1, \mathbf{e}_2, \ldots, \mathbf{e}_n\}$ be a basis for $\mathbb{R}^n$. The **transition matrix $\mathbf{P}$** from the basis E to the standard basis for $\mathbb{R}^n$ is the matrix whose jth column is formed from the standard coordinates of $\mathbf{e}_j$.

Exercise 2.5

  (a) Write down the transition matrix $\mathbf{P}$ from the basis
      $E = \{(1,3), (2,5)\}$ to the standard basis for $\mathbb{R}^2$.

  (b) Write down the transition matrix $\mathbf{P}$ from the basis
      $E = \{(0, 1, -1), (-2, 1, 0), (1, 0, -1)\}$ to the standard basis for $\mathbb{R}^3$.

In the example above, we have seen that the transition matrix $\mathbf{P}$ from the basis $E = \{(1, -2), (3, 1)\}$ to the standard basis for $\mathbb{R}^2$ converts E-coordinate representations into standard coordinate representations and that $\mathbf{P}^{-1}$ converts standard coordinate representations into E-coordinate representations. This is true in general.

Theorem 2.2   Let $E = \{\mathbf{e}_1, \mathbf{e}_2, \ldots, \mathbf{e}_n\}$ be a basis for $\mathbb{R}^n$ and let $\mathbf{P}$ be the transition matrix from the basis E to the standard basis for $\mathbb{R}^n$. Then the standard coordinate representation of a vector in $\mathbb{R}^n$ is given by

$$\mathbf{v} = \mathbf{P}\mathbf{v}_E.$$

Moreover, $\mathbf{P}$ is invertible and

$$\mathbf{v}_E = \mathbf{P}^{-1}\mathbf{v}.$$

Proof   The statement $\mathbf{v} = \mathbf{P}\mathbf{v}_E$ is equivalent to the statement that $\mathbf{P}$ is the matrix of the identity transformation i of $\mathbb{R}^n$ with respect to the basis E for the domain and the standard basis for the codomain.

To find this matrix $\mathbf{P}$, we use Strategy 2.1. We begin by finding the images under i of the vectors in the domain basis E:

$$i(\mathbf{e}_1) = \mathbf{e}_1, \quad i(\mathbf{e}_2) = \mathbf{e}_2, \quad \ldots, \quad i(\mathbf{e}_n) = \mathbf{e}_n.$$

It now follows from Strategy 2.1 that each column of $\mathbf{P}$ is formed from the standard coordinates of the corresponding basis vector, so $\mathbf{P}$ is the transition matrix from the basis E to the standard basis for $\mathbb{R}^n$, as claimed.

We know that the identity transformation i is invertible and that $i^{-1} = i$. It follows from the Inverse Rule that $\mathbf{P}$ is invertible and that $\mathbf{P}^{-1}$ is the matrix of $i : \mathbb{R}^n \longrightarrow \mathbb{R}^n$ with respect to the standard basis for the domain and the basis E for the codomain; that is,

Unit LA4, Theorem 3.2.

$$\mathbf{v} \longmapsto \mathbf{v}_E = \mathbf{P}^{-1}\mathbf{v}. \quad \blacksquare$$

Remarks

1. When E is the standard basis for $\mathbb{R}^n$, the matrix $\mathbf{P}$ is the identity matrix $\mathbf{I}_n$, as you would expect.

2. A consequence of Theorem 2.2 is that if the rows or columns of an $n \times n$ matrix $\mathbf{A}$ form a set of n linearly independent vectors, then $\det \mathbf{A} \neq 0$. For, if the columns are linearly independent, then the columns form a basis for $\mathbb{R}^n$ and $\mathbf{A}$ is the transition matrix from this basis to the standard basis. Hence $\mathbf{A}$ is invertible, so $\det \mathbf{A} \neq 0$. If the rows are linearly independent, then we find that $\det \mathbf{A}^T = \det \mathbf{A} \neq 0$ on applying the above reasoning to $\mathbf{A}^T$.

    Unit LA2, Theorem 5.4.

    Unit LA2, Theorem 5.1.

    The converse of this result is also true: if $\det \mathbf{A} \neq 0$, then the rows or columns of $\mathbf{A}$ form a linearly independent set of vectors. For, if the rows of $\mathbf{A}$ form a linearly dependent set, then the row-reduced form of $\mathbf{A}$ contains a zero row, so $\mathbf{A}$ is not invertible and hence $\det \mathbf{A} = 0$. If the columns of $\mathbf{A}$ form a linearly dependent set, then the same argument can be applied to $\mathbf{A}^T$ to show that $\det \mathbf{A} = \det \mathbf{A}^T = 0$.

    Unit LA2, Theorem 4.5.

Recall that our aim in this subsection is to relate the matrices $\mathbf{D}$ and $\mathbf{A}$, where $\mathbf{D}$ is the matrix of a linear transformation $t : \mathbb{R}^n \longrightarrow \mathbb{R}^n$ with respect to an eigenvector basis of t, and $\mathbf{A}$ is the matrix of t with respect to the standard basis for $\mathbb{R}^n$. The following diagram shows how we can do this by using the transition matrix $\mathbf{P}$ from the eigenvector basis E to the standard basis for $\mathbb{R}^n$.

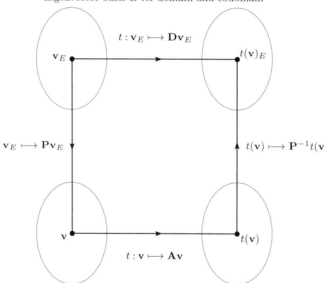

Eigenvector basis E for domain and codomain

Standard basis for domain and codomain

The top line of the diagram shows that multiplication by $\mathbf{D}$ converts the E-coordinate representation of $\mathbf{v}$ to the E-coordinate representation of $t(\mathbf{v})$:

$$t(\mathbf{v})_E = \mathbf{D}\mathbf{v}_E. \tag{2.1}$$

The diagram also shows that this change can be achieved in another way, in three steps.

1. Use the transition matrix $\mathbf{P}$ to convert the E-coordinate representation of $\mathbf{v}$ to the standard coordinate representation of $\mathbf{v}$:

    $$\mathbf{v} = \mathbf{P}\mathbf{v}_E.$$

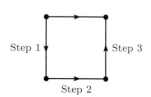

2. Apply the matrix $\mathbf{A}$ to $\mathbf{v}$ to obtain the standard coordinate representation of $t(\mathbf{v})$:

$$t(\mathbf{v}) = \mathbf{A}\mathbf{v} = \mathbf{A}\mathbf{P}\mathbf{v}_E.$$

3. Use the matrix $\mathbf{P}^{-1}$ to convert the standard coordinate representation of $t(\mathbf{v})$ to the E-coordinate representation of $t(\mathbf{v})$:

$$t(\mathbf{v})_E = \mathbf{P}^{-1}t(\mathbf{v}) = \mathbf{P}^{-1}\mathbf{A}\mathbf{P}\mathbf{v}_E.$$

Comparing this last equation with equation (2.1), we see that $\mathbf{D}$, $\mathbf{A}$ and $\mathbf{P}$ are related by the equation

$$\mathbf{D} = \mathbf{P}^{-1}\mathbf{A}\mathbf{P}.$$

Thus we have proved the following result.

Theorem 2.3   Let $t : \mathbb{R}^n \longrightarrow \mathbb{R}^n$ be a linear transformation and let E be an eigenvector basis of t. Let $\mathbf{A}$ be the matrix of t with respect to the standard basis for $\mathbb{R}^n$, let $\mathbf{D}$ be the matrix of t with respect to the eigenvector basis E and let $\mathbf{P}$ be the transition matrix from E to the standard basis for $\mathbb{R}^n$. Then

$$\mathbf{D} = \mathbf{P}^{-1}\mathbf{A}\mathbf{P}.$$

Remark   Theorem 2.3 holds for *any* basis E for $\mathbb{R}^n$, although $\mathbf{D}$ is diagonal only when E is an eigenvector basis.

We end this subsection by applying Theorem 2.3 to some examples.

Consider the linear transformation $t : \mathbb{R}^2 \longrightarrow \mathbb{R}^2$ given by

$$t(x, y) = (x + 3y, 2x - 4y).$$

In Example 2.1 you saw that

$$\mathbf{A} = \begin{pmatrix} 1 & 3 \\ 2 & -4 \end{pmatrix}$$

is the matrix of t with respect to the standard basis for $\mathbb{R}^2$ and that

$$\mathbf{D} = \begin{pmatrix} -5 & 0 \\ 0 & 2 \end{pmatrix}$$

is the matrix of t with respect to the eigenvector basis $E = \{(1, -2), (3, 1)\}$.

At the beginning of this subsection you saw that the transition matrix from the basis E to the standard basis for $\mathbb{R}^2$ is

See page 22.

$$\mathbf{P} = \begin{pmatrix} 1 & 3 \\ -2 & 1 \end{pmatrix},$$

so

$$\begin{aligned} \mathbf{P}^{-1}\mathbf{A}\mathbf{P} &= \begin{pmatrix} \frac{1}{7} & -\frac{3}{7} \\ \frac{2}{7} & \frac{1}{7} \end{pmatrix} \begin{pmatrix} 1 & 3 \\ 2 & -4 \end{pmatrix} \begin{pmatrix} 1 & 3 \\ -2 & 1 \end{pmatrix} \\ &= \begin{pmatrix} -5 & 0 \\ 0 & 2 \end{pmatrix} \\ &= \mathbf{D}, \end{aligned}$$

You saw how to find the inverse of a 2×2 matrix in Unit LA2, Strategy 5.1.

as claimed.

25

Exercise 2.6 Use the solution to Exercise 2.3 to find a matrix $\mathbf{P}$ such that $\mathbf{D} = \mathbf{P}^{-1}\mathbf{AP}$, where

$$\mathbf{A} = \begin{pmatrix} 1 & -2 \\ -2 & -2 \end{pmatrix} \quad \text{and} \quad \mathbf{D} = \begin{pmatrix} 2 & 0 \\ 0 & -3 \end{pmatrix}.$$

2.3 Diagonalisation

In this subsection we consider the problem of determining when a matrix is *diagonalisable*.

Definition The matrix $\mathbf{A}$ is **diagonalisable** if there exists an invertible matrix $\mathbf{P}$ such that the matrix

$$\mathbf{D} = \mathbf{P}^{-1}\mathbf{AP}$$

is diagonal.

The matrices $\mathbf{A}$, $\mathbf{D}$ and $\mathbf{P}$ must all be square matrices of the same size.

Note that if $\mathbf{D} = \mathbf{P}^{-1}\mathbf{AP}$, then $\mathbf{PD} = \mathbf{AP}$, so

$$\mathbf{PDP}^{-1} = \mathbf{APP}^{-1} = \mathbf{A}.$$

Similarly,

$$\mathbf{PD}^2\mathbf{P}^{-1} = \mathbf{P}(\mathbf{P}^{-1}\mathbf{AP})(\mathbf{P}^{-1}\mathbf{AP})\mathbf{P}^{-1} = \mathbf{A}^2$$

and, in general,

$$\mathbf{PD}^n\mathbf{P}^{-1} = \mathbf{A}^n, \quad \text{for } n = 1, 2, \dots.$$

This last equation is useful for calculating powers of matrices, since calculating the nth power of a diagonal matrix is particularly simple—you need to find only the nth power of each diagonal entry.

Exercise 2.7

(a) Write down $\mathbf{D}^5$, where $\mathbf{D} = \begin{pmatrix} 2 & 0 \\ 0 & -3 \end{pmatrix}$.

(b) Use the solution to Exercise 2.6 to calculate $\mathbf{A}^5$, where

$$\mathbf{A} = \begin{pmatrix} 1 & -2 \\ -2 & -2 \end{pmatrix}.$$

If $\mathbf{A}$ is any $n \times n$ matrix, then we can define a linear transformation t as:

$$t : \mathbb{R}^n \longrightarrow \mathbb{R}^n$$

$$\mathbf{v} \longmapsto \mathbf{Av}.$$

In Section 1 we said that $\mathbf{v}$ is an eigenvector of $\mathbf{A}$ with corresponding eigenvalue λ if $\mathbf{Av} = t(\mathbf{v}) = \lambda\mathbf{v}$; that is, if $\mathbf{v}$ is an eigenvector of t.

Definition Let $\mathbf{A}$ be an $n \times n$ matrix and let $E = \{\mathbf{e}_1, \dots, \mathbf{e}_n\}$ be a basis for $\mathbb{R}^n$ consisting of eigenvectors of $\mathbf{A}$. The basis E is an **eigenvector basis** of $\mathbf{A}$.

Thus E is an eigenvector basis of $\mathbf{A}$ if E is an eigenvector basis of t.

Example 2.2   Find an eigenvector basis of the matrix

$$\mathbf{A} = \begin{pmatrix} 5 & 2 \\ 2 & 5 \end{pmatrix}.$$

Solution   In Example 1.2 you saw that the eigenvectors of $\mathbf{A}$ are the non-zero vectors of the forms

(k, k), corresponding to the eigenvalue $\lambda = 7$,

and

$(k, -k)$, corresponding to the eigenvalue $\lambda = 3$.

Since $(1, 1)$ and $(1, -1)$ are eigenvectors of $\mathbf{A}$, and $(1, -1)$ is not a multiple of $(1, 1)$, the set $E = \{(1, 1), (1, -1)\}$ is an eigenvector basis of $\mathbf{A}$.   ∎

Suppose that E is an eigenvector basis of the $n \times n$ matrix $\mathbf{A}$; that is, E is an eigenvector basis of the linear transformation $t : \mathbb{R}^n \longrightarrow \mathbb{R}^n$ given by

$$t(\mathbf{v}) = \mathbf{A}\mathbf{v}.$$

It follows from Theorems 2.1 and 2.3 that if $\mathbf{P}$ is the transition matrix from the basis E to the standard basis for $\mathbb{R}^n$, then

$$\mathbf{D} = \mathbf{P}^{-1}\mathbf{A}\mathbf{P}$$

is diagonal; that is, $\mathbf{A}$ is diagonalisable. This gives the following strategy for diagonalising a matrix, when this is possible.

Strategy 2.2   To diagonalise an $n \times n$ matrix $\mathbf{A}$.

1.   Find all the eigenvalues of $\mathbf{A}$.

2.   Find (if possible) an eigenvector basis $E = \{\mathbf{e}_1, \dots, \mathbf{e}_n\}$ of $\mathbf{A}$.

3.   Write down the transition matrix $\mathbf{P}$ whose jth column is formed from the standard coordinates of $\mathbf{e}_j$.

4.   Then

$$\mathbf{P}^{-1}\mathbf{A}\mathbf{P} = \mathbf{D} = \begin{pmatrix} \lambda_1 & 0 & \cdots & 0 \\ 0 & \lambda_2 & \cdots & 0 \\ \vdots & \vdots & & \vdots \\ 0 & 0 & \cdots & \lambda_n \end{pmatrix},$$

where λ_j is the eigenvalue corresponding to the eigenvector $\mathbf{e}_j$.

The difficulty of finding an eigenvector basis of $\mathbf{A}$ in step 2 of Strategy 2.2 depends on the matrix $\mathbf{A}$. In Example 2.2 we formed an eigenvector basis of $\mathbf{A}$ by taking one eigenvector corresponding to each eigenvalue. In general, we have the following result.

Theorem 2.4   Let $\mathbf{A}$ be an $n \times n$ matrix with distinct eigenvalues $\lambda_1, \lambda_2, \dots, \lambda_n$ and corresponding eigenvectors $\mathbf{e}_1, \mathbf{e}_2, \dots, \mathbf{e}_n$. Then $E = \{\mathbf{e}_1, \mathbf{e}_2, \dots, \mathbf{e}_n\}$ is an eigenvector basis of $\mathbf{A}$.

We prove this result at the end of the section.

We give an example showing how Theorem 2.4 can be used.

Example 2.3   Diagonalise the matrix

$$\mathbf{A} = \begin{pmatrix} 2 & 0 & 1 \\ -1 & 2 & 3 \\ 1 & 0 & 2 \end{pmatrix}.$$

Solution   We use Strategy 2.2.

The eigenvalues of $\mathbf{A}$ are $\lambda = 3$, $\lambda = 2$ and $\lambda = 1$.

The eigenvectors of $\mathbf{A}$ are the non-zero vectors of the forms

$(k, 2k, k)$, corresponding to $\lambda = 3$,

$(0, k, 0)$, corresponding to $\lambda = 2$,

and

$(k, 4k, -k)$, corresponding to $\lambda = 1$.

We found the eigenvalues and eigenvectors of $\mathbf{A}$ in Example 1.3.

It follows from Theorem 2.4 that we can form an eigenvector basis of $\mathbf{A}$ by taking one eigenvector corresponding to each of the three distinct eigenvalues. For example,

$E = \{(1, 2, 1), (0, 1, 0), (1, 4, -1)\}$

is an eigenvector basis of $\mathbf{A}$.

We use the eigenvectors in E to form the columns of the transition matrix:

$$\mathbf{P} = \begin{pmatrix} 1 & 0 & 1 \\ 2 & 1 & 4 \\ 1 & 0 & -1 \end{pmatrix}.$$

We use the eigenvalues corresponding to the eigenvectors in E to form the diagonal matrix:

$$\mathbf{P}^{-1}\mathbf{A}\mathbf{P} = \mathbf{D} = \begin{pmatrix} 3 & 0 & 0 \\ 0 & 2 & 0 \\ 0 & 0 & 1 \end{pmatrix}. \quad \blacksquare$$

The eigenvalues in $\mathbf{D}$ must appear in the same order as the corresponding eigenvectors in $\mathbf{P}$.

Exercise 2.8   Diagonalise the matrix

$$\mathbf{A} = \begin{pmatrix} 4 & 2 & 0 \\ 2 & 3 & 2 \\ 0 & 2 & 2 \end{pmatrix}.$$

Use the solution to Exercise 1.6.

It may be possible to find an eigenvector basis of an $n \times n$ matrix $\mathbf{A}$, even when $\mathbf{A}$ does not have n distinct eigenvalues.

Strategy 2.3   To find an eigenvector basis of an $n \times n$ matrix $\mathbf{A}$.

1. Find a basis for each eigenspace of $\mathbf{A}$.

2. Form the set E of all the basis vectors found in step 1.

    If there are n vectors in E, then E is an eigenvector basis of $\mathbf{A}$; otherwise E is not a basis.

This can be proved in a similar way to Theorem 2.4, but the details are more complicated.

Example 2.4   Diagonalise the matrix

$$\mathbf{A} = \begin{pmatrix} 4 & 2 & 2 \\ 2 & 4 & 2 \\ 2 & 2 & 4 \end{pmatrix}.$$

Solution   The eigenvalues of $\mathbf{A}$ are $\lambda = 8$, $\lambda = 2$ and $\lambda = 2$.

You found the eigenvalues and eigenspaces of $\mathbf{A}$ in Exercise 1.9.

The eigenspaces of $\mathbf{A}$ are

$S(8) = \{(k, k, k) : k \in \mathbb{R}\}$ and $S(2) = \{(k, l, -k - l) : k, l \in \mathbb{R}\}$.

A basis for $S(8)$ is $\{(1, 1, 1)\}$ and a basis for $S(2)$ is $\{(1, 0, -1), (0, 1, -1)\}$.

Since the set

$$E = \{(1,1,1),(1,0,-1),(0,1,-1)\}$$

contains three vectors, it is an eigenvector basis of $\mathbf{A}$.

We use the eigenvectors in E to form the columns of the transition matrix:

$$\mathbf{P} = \begin{pmatrix} 1 & 1 & 0 \\ 1 & 0 & 1 \\ 1 & -1 & -1 \end{pmatrix}.$$

We use the eigenvalues corresponding to the eigenvectors in E to form the diagonal matrix:

$$\mathbf{P}^{-1}\mathbf{A}\mathbf{P} = \mathbf{D} = \begin{pmatrix} 8 & 0 & 0 \\ 0 & 2 & 0 \\ 0 & 0 & 2 \end{pmatrix}. \quad \blacksquare$$

Exercise 2.9   Diagonalise the matrix

$$\begin{pmatrix} 1 & 0 & 0 \\ 0 & 2 & 1 \\ 0 & 1 & 2 \end{pmatrix}.$$

If the matrix $\mathbf{A}$ does *not* have an eigenvector basis, then these methods cannot be applied and the matrix $\mathbf{A}$ is not diagonalisable. For example, in Section 1 you saw that all the eigenvectors of the matrix

$$\mathbf{A} = \begin{pmatrix} 1 & 1 \\ 0 & 1 \end{pmatrix}$$

See Exercise 1.10.

are non-zero vectors of the form $(k,0)$. Any two eigenvectors of $\mathbf{A}$ are linearly dependent, so there is no eigenvector basis. Thus $\mathbf{A}$ is not diagonalisable.

We end this section by proving Theorem 2.4.

Theorem 2.4   Let $\mathbf{A}$ be an $n \times n$ matrix with distinct eigenvalues $\lambda_1, \lambda_2, \ldots, \lambda_n$ and corresponding eigenvectors $\mathbf{e}_1, \mathbf{e}_2, \ldots, \mathbf{e}_n$. Then $E = \{\mathbf{e}_1, \mathbf{e}_2, \ldots, \mathbf{e}_n\}$ is an eigenvector basis of $\mathbf{A}$.

Proof   Let $\mathbf{A}$ and E be as in the statement of the theorem. Any linearly independent set of n vectors in $\mathbb{R}^n$ is a basis for $\mathbb{R}^n$, so we need show only that E is linearly independent. To do this, we assume that E is linearly dependent and obtain a contradiction.

Unit LA3, Subsection 3.4.

Suppose that E is linearly dependent. Then we can take the smallest value of m ($2 \leq m \leq n$) for which a set of m vectors in E is linearly dependent. By relabelling the eigenvectors (if necessary), we can write

$$\alpha_1\mathbf{e}_1 + \alpha_2\mathbf{e}_2 + \cdots + \alpha_m\mathbf{e}_m = \mathbf{0}, \tag{2.2}$$

with $\alpha_1 \neq 0$, $\alpha_2 \neq 0$, $\ldots$, $\alpha_m \neq 0$.

Applying the matrix $\mathbf{A}$ to both sides of equation (2.2), we obtain

$$\mathbf{A}(\alpha_1\mathbf{e}_1 + \alpha_2\mathbf{e}_2 + \cdots + \alpha_m\mathbf{e}_m) = \mathbf{A}\mathbf{0},$$

that is,

$$\alpha_1\mathbf{A}\mathbf{e}_1 + \alpha_2\mathbf{A}\mathbf{e}_2 + \cdots + \alpha_m\mathbf{A}\mathbf{e}_m = \mathbf{0}.$$

Now, $\mathbf{e}_1, \mathbf{e}_2, \ldots, \mathbf{e}_m$ are eigenvectors of $\mathbf{A}$ with corresponding eigenvalues $\lambda_1, \lambda_2, \ldots, \lambda_m$, so $\mathbf{A}\mathbf{e}_j = \lambda_j \mathbf{e}_j$ and

$$\alpha_1 \lambda_1 \mathbf{e}_1 + \alpha_2 \lambda_2 \mathbf{e}_2 + \cdots + \alpha_m \lambda_m \mathbf{e}_m = \mathbf{0}. \tag{2.3}$$

We now eliminate the vector $\mathbf{e}_m$. To do this, we multiply equation (2.2) by λ_m and subtract the result from equation (2.3):

$$\alpha_1(\lambda_1 - \lambda_m)\mathbf{e}_1 + \alpha_2(\lambda_2 - \lambda_m)\mathbf{e}_2 + \cdots + \alpha_{m-1}(\lambda_{m-1} - \lambda_m)\mathbf{e}_{m-1} = \mathbf{0}.$$

Since the eigenvalues $\lambda_1, \lambda_2, \ldots, \lambda_{m-1}$ are distinct, and none of the numbers $\alpha_1, \alpha_2, \ldots, \alpha_{m-1}$ is zero, we deduce that the set of $m - 1$ vectors $\{\mathbf{e}_1, \mathbf{e}_2, \ldots, \mathbf{e}_{m-1}\}$ is linearly dependent. This, however, is impossible since m is the *smallest* number such that a set of m vectors in E is linearly dependent. This contradiction establishes the result. ∎

Further exercises

Exercise 2.10   Let $t : \mathbb{R}^2 \longrightarrow \mathbb{R}^2$ be the linear transformation given by

$$t(x, y) = (x + y, x + y).$$

(a) Write down the matrix $\mathbf{A}$ of t with respect to the standard basis for $\mathbb{R}^2$.

(b) Find an eigenvector basis E of t.

(c) Find the matrix $\mathbf{D}$ of t with respect to the basis E.

(d) Find a matrix $\mathbf{P}$ such that $\mathbf{P}^{-1}\mathbf{A}\mathbf{P} = \mathbf{D}$.

Exercise 2.11   Use the solution to Exercise 1.12 to diagonalise the matrix

$$\mathbf{A} = \begin{pmatrix} -5 & 3 \\ 6 & -2 \end{pmatrix}.$$

Exercise 2.12   Use the solution to Exercise 1.13 to diagonalise the matrix

$$\mathbf{A} = \begin{pmatrix} 3 & 2 & 2 \\ -2 & -2 & -2 \\ 1 & 2 & 2 \end{pmatrix}.$$

Exercise 2.13   Use the solution to Exercise 1.15 to diagonalise the matrix

$$\mathbf{A} = \begin{pmatrix} 0 & 0 & -2 \\ 1 & 2 & 1 \\ 1 & 0 & 3 \end{pmatrix}.$$

3   Symmetric matrices

After working through this section, you should be able to:

(a) understand that any symmetric matrix can be *orthogonally diagonalised*;

(b) orthogonally diagonalise a given symmetric matrix;

(c) describe some basic properties of *orthogonal matrices*.

3.1 Diagonalising symmetric matrices

Suppose that $\mathbf{A}$ is an $n \times n$ matrix and that we can find a basis $\{\mathbf{e}_1, \ldots, \mathbf{e}_n\}$ for $\mathbb{R}^n$ consisting of eigenvectors of $\mathbf{A}$. In Section 2 you saw that $\mathbf{A}$ can be diagonalised. If $\mathbf{P}$ is the transition matrix whose columns are formed from the coordinates of the eigenvectors $\mathbf{e}_1, \ldots, \mathbf{e}_n$, then

$$\mathbf{P}^{-1}\mathbf{A}\mathbf{P}$$

is a diagonal matrix.

In this section we see that whenever $\mathbf{A}$ is an $n \times n$ *symmetric* matrix, then we can always find a basis for $\mathbb{R}^n$ made up of eigenvectors of $\mathbf{A}$, and so such a matrix is always diagonalisable. In fact, we can always find an *orthonormal* basis for $\mathbb{R}^n$ made up of eigenvectors of $\mathbf{A}$. In this case, the transition matrix $\mathbf{P}$ has the extra property that $\mathbf{P}^{-1} = \mathbf{P}^T$, so

$$\mathbf{P}^T\mathbf{A}\mathbf{P}$$

$\mathbf{A}^T = \mathbf{A}$

An *orthonormal* basis consists of mutually perpendicular (*orthogonal*) vectors of unit length (Unit LA3, Section 5). For example, the standard basis for $\mathbb{R}^n$ is an orthonormal basis.

is a diagonal matrix. Finding the transpose of a matrix is much simpler than finding the inverse, so this is a useful result.

For example, consider the symmetric matrix

$$\mathbf{A} = \begin{pmatrix} 4 & 2 & 0 \\ 2 & 3 & 2 \\ 0 & 2 & 2 \end{pmatrix}.$$

We shall show that there is an orthonormal basis for $\mathbb{R}^3$ which consists of eigenvectors of $\mathbf{A}$.

The eigenvalues of $\mathbf{A}$ are $\lambda = 6$, $\lambda = 3$ and $\lambda = 0$. The eigenvectors are the non-zero vectors of the forms

You found these eigenvalues and eigenvectors in Exercise 1.6.

$(2k, 2k, k)$, corresponding to $\lambda = 6$,

$(-2k, k, 2k)$, corresponding to $\lambda = 3$,

and

$(k, -2k, 2k)$, corresponding to $\lambda = 0$.

Exercise 3.1   Let

$$\mathbf{v}_1 = (2k, 2k, k), \quad \mathbf{v}_2 = (-2l, l, 2l), \quad \mathbf{v}_3 = (m, -2m, 2m),$$

where k, l, m are positive numbers.

(a) Show that $\{\mathbf{v}_1, \mathbf{v}_2, \mathbf{v}_3\}$ is an *orthogonal* basis for $\mathbb{R}^3$.

(b) Find values of k, l and m for which $\|\mathbf{v}_1\| = \|\mathbf{v}_2\| = \|\mathbf{v}_3\| = 1$.

In Unit LA3, Section 5, you saw that $\{\mathbf{v}_1, \ldots, \mathbf{v}_n\}$ is an orthonormal basis for $\mathbb{R}^n$ if $\mathbf{v}_i \cdot \mathbf{v}_j = 0$ for $i \neq j$, and $\|\mathbf{v}_i\| = 1$ for each i. It follows from Exercise 3.1 that

$$E = \left\{ \left(\tfrac{2}{3}, \tfrac{2}{3}, \tfrac{1}{3}\right), \left(-\tfrac{2}{3}, \tfrac{1}{3}, \tfrac{2}{3}\right), \left(\tfrac{1}{3}, -\tfrac{2}{3}, \tfrac{2}{3}\right) \right\}$$

is an orthonormal basis for $\mathbb{R}^3$. Since E is an eigenvector basis of $\mathbf{A}$, we say that E is an *orthonormal eigenvector basis* of $\mathbf{A}$.

Following Strategy 2.2, we diagonalise the matrix $\mathbf{A}$ by writing down the transition matrix $\mathbf{P}$ whose columns are formed from the coordinates of the vectors in E:

$$\mathbf{P} = \begin{pmatrix} \frac{2}{3} & -\frac{2}{3} & \frac{1}{3} \\ \frac{2}{3} & \frac{1}{3} & -\frac{2}{3} \\ \frac{1}{3} & \frac{2}{3} & \frac{2}{3} \end{pmatrix}.$$

A transition matrix formed from an orthonormal eigenvector basis in this way is called an *orthogonal* matrix.

Definition   An $n \times n$ matrix whose columns form an orthonormal basis for $\mathbb{R}^n$ is an **orthogonal** matrix.

For example, the 2×2 matrix

$$\begin{pmatrix} \frac{1}{\sqrt{2}} & \frac{1}{\sqrt{2}} \\ \frac{1}{\sqrt{2}} & -\frac{1}{\sqrt{2}} \end{pmatrix}$$

is orthogonal, since

$$\left(\frac{1}{\sqrt{2}}\right)^2 + \left(\frac{1}{\sqrt{2}}\right)^2 = 1, \quad \left(\frac{1}{\sqrt{2}}\right)^2 + \left(-\frac{1}{\sqrt{2}}\right)^2 = 1$$

and

$$\left(\frac{1}{\sqrt{2}}, \frac{1}{\sqrt{2}}\right) \cdot \left(\frac{1}{\sqrt{2}}, -\frac{1}{\sqrt{2}}\right) = 0.$$

Exercise 3.2   Let

$$\mathbf{P} = \begin{pmatrix} \frac{2}{3} & -\frac{2}{3} & \frac{1}{3} \\ \frac{2}{3} & \frac{1}{3} & -\frac{2}{3} \\ \frac{1}{3} & \frac{2}{3} & \frac{2}{3} \end{pmatrix}.$$

Show that $\mathbf{P}^T \mathbf{P} = \mathbf{I}$ and deduce that $\mathbf{P}^T = \mathbf{P}^{-1}$.

In Subsection 3.2 we prove that $\mathbf{P}^T = \mathbf{P}^{-1}$ for any orthogonal matrix $\mathbf{P}$.

It follows from Exercise 3.2 and Strategy 2.2 that

$$\mathbf{P}^T \mathbf{A} \mathbf{P} = \mathbf{P}^{-1} \mathbf{A} \mathbf{P} = \begin{pmatrix} 6 & 0 & 0 \\ 0 & 3 & 0 \\ 0 & 0 & 0 \end{pmatrix}.$$

We say that the matrix $\mathbf{A}$ has been *orthogonally diagonalised*.

Definition   The matrix $\mathbf{A}$ is **orthogonally diagonalisable** if there exists an orthogonal matrix $\mathbf{P}$ such that the matrix

$$\mathbf{D} = \mathbf{P}^T \mathbf{A} \mathbf{P} = \mathbf{P}^{-1} \mathbf{A} \mathbf{P}$$

is diagonal.

The following strategy is a modification of Strategy 2.2 for diagonalising a matrix.

Strategy 3.1   To orthogonally diagonalise an $n \times n$ symmetric matrix $\mathbf{A}$.

1. Find all the eigenvalues of $\mathbf{A}$.

2. Find an orthonormal eigenvector basis $E = \{\mathbf{e}_1, \mathbf{e}_2, \ldots, \mathbf{e}_n\}$ of $\mathbf{A}$.

3. Write down the orthogonal transition matrix $\mathbf{P}$ whose jth column is formed from the standard coordinates of $\mathbf{e}_j$.

4. Then

$$\mathbf{P}^T \mathbf{A} \mathbf{P} = \mathbf{D} = \begin{pmatrix} \lambda_1 & 0 & \cdots & 0 \\ 0 & \lambda_2 & \cdots & 0 \\ \vdots & \vdots & & \vdots \\ 0 & 0 & \cdots & \lambda_n \end{pmatrix},$$

where λ_j is the eigenvalue corresponding to the eigenvector $\mathbf{e}_j$.

> If our aim is simply to diagonalise the matrix, then we use Strategy 2.2—this saves time and effort when an orthonormal basis is not required. Read the questions carefully!

You may have noticed that the words 'if possible' appear in Strategy 2.2, but not in Strategy 3.1. An $n \times n$ symmetric matrix $\mathbf{A}$ *always* has an orthonormal eigenvector basis, so it must be orthogonally diagonalisable. In the case where $\mathbf{A}$ has n distinct eigenvalues, this follows from the following result.

> It is also true that any orthogonally diagonalisable matrix $\mathbf{A}$ must be symmetric.

Theorem 3.1   Eigenvectors corresponding to distinct eigenvalues of a symmetric matrix are orthogonal.

> In Unit LA3, Section 5, you saw that an orthogonal set of n non-zero vectors in $\mathbb{R}^n$ is an orthogonal basis for $\mathbb{R}^n$.

We give an example showing how Theorem 3.1 can be used.

> We prove Theorem 3.1 at the end of the subsection.

Example 3.1   Orthogonally diagonalise the symmetric matrix

$$\mathbf{A} = \begin{pmatrix} 5 & 2 \\ 2 & 5 \end{pmatrix}.$$

Solution   We use Strategy 3.1.

The eigenvalues of $\mathbf{A}$ are $\lambda = 7$ and $\lambda = 3$.

The eigenvectors of $\mathbf{A}$ are the non-zero vectors of the forms

> We found the eigenvalues and eigenvectors of $\mathbf{A}$ in Example 1.2.

(k, k), corresponding to $\lambda = 7$,

and

$(k, -k)$, corresponding to $\lambda = 3$.

It follows from Theorem 3.1 that we can form an orthonormal eigenvector basis of $\mathbf{A}$ by taking an eigenvector of unit length corresponding to each of the two distinct eigenvalues. For example,

$$E = \left\{ \left(\tfrac{1}{\sqrt{2}}, \tfrac{1}{\sqrt{2}} \right), \left(-\tfrac{1}{\sqrt{2}}, \tfrac{1}{\sqrt{2}} \right) \right\}$$

is an orthonormal eigenvector basis of $\mathbf{A}$.

Using the eigenvectors in E, we form the orthogonal transition matrix:

$$\mathbf{P} = \begin{pmatrix} \tfrac{1}{\sqrt{2}} & -\tfrac{1}{\sqrt{2}} \\ \tfrac{1}{\sqrt{2}} & \tfrac{1}{\sqrt{2}} \end{pmatrix}.$$

33

We use the eigenvalues corresponding to the eigenvectors in E to form the diagonal matrix:

$$\mathbf{P}^T\mathbf{A}\mathbf{P} = \mathbf{D} = \begin{pmatrix} 7 & 0 \\ 0 & 3 \end{pmatrix}. \quad \blacksquare$$

Exercise 3.3 Orthogonally diagonalise each of the following symmetric matrices.

(a) $\mathbf{A} = \begin{pmatrix} 9 & -2 \\ -2 & 6 \end{pmatrix}$ (b) $\mathbf{A} = \begin{pmatrix} 5 & -1 & -1 \\ -1 & 3 & 1 \\ -1 & 1 & 3 \end{pmatrix}$

In part (b) the eigenvalues are $\lambda = 6$, $\lambda = 3$ and $\lambda = 2$.

We now give a general strategy for finding an orthonormal eigenvector basis of a symmetric matrix.

Strategy 3.2 To find an orthonormal eigenvector basis of an $n \times n$ symmetric matrix $\mathbf{A}$.

1. Find an orthonormal basis for each eigenspace of $\mathbf{A}$.

2. Form the set E of all the basis vectors found in step 1. This is the required basis.

Example 3.2   Orthogonally diagonalise the symmetric matrix

$$\mathbf{A} = \begin{pmatrix} 4 & 2 & 2 \\ 2 & 4 & 2 \\ 2 & 2 & 4 \end{pmatrix}.$$

Solution   The eigenvalues of $\mathbf{A}$ are $\lambda = 8$, $\lambda = 2$ and $\lambda = 2$.

You found the eigenvalues and eigenspaces of $\mathbf{A}$ in Exercise 1.9.

The eigenvectors of $\mathbf{A}$ are the non-zero vectors of the forms

(k, k, k), corresponding to $\lambda = 8$,

and

$(k, l, -(k + l))$, corresponding to $\lambda = 2$.

Now, $(k, k, k) = k(1, 1, 1)$ so a basis for the eigenspace $S(8)$ is $\{(1, 1, 1)\}$.

An orthonormal basis for $S(8)$ is

$$\left\{ \left(\tfrac{1}{\sqrt{3}}, \tfrac{1}{\sqrt{3}}, \tfrac{1}{\sqrt{3}} \right) \right\}.$$

Also,

$(k, l, -(k + l)) = k(1, 0, -1) + l(0, 1, -1)$,

so a basis for the eigenspace $S(2)$ is $\{(1, 0, -1), (0, 1, -1)\}$.

To find an *orthogonal* basis for the eigenspace $S(2)$, we use the Gram–Schmidt orthogonalisation process.

This method for finding an orthogonal basis was given in Unit LA3, Subsection 5.2.

Let the orthogonal basis we seek be $\{\mathbf{v}_1, \mathbf{v}_2\}$.

Let $\mathbf{v}_1 = (1, 0, -1)$.

Then let

$$\mathbf{v}_2 = (0, 1, -1) - \left(\frac{\mathbf{v}_1 \cdot (0, 1, -1)}{\mathbf{v}_1 \cdot \mathbf{v}_1} \right) \mathbf{v}_1$$

$$= (0, 1, -1) - \left(\frac{(1, 0, -1) \cdot (0, 1, -1)}{(1, 0, -1) \cdot (1, 0, -1)} \right) (1, 0, -1)$$

$$= (0, 1, -1) - \tfrac{1}{2}(1, 0, -1)$$

$$= (-\tfrac{1}{2}, 1, -\tfrac{1}{2}).$$

An orthonormal basis for $S(2)$ is therefore

$$\left\{ \left(\tfrac{1}{\sqrt{2}}, 0, -\tfrac{1}{\sqrt{2}} \right), \left(\tfrac{1}{\sqrt{6}}, -\tfrac{2}{\sqrt{6}}, \tfrac{1}{\sqrt{6}} \right) \right\}.$$

An orthonormal eigenvector basis of $\mathbf{A}$ is therefore

$$E = \left\{ \left(\tfrac{1}{\sqrt{3}}, \tfrac{1}{\sqrt{3}}, \tfrac{1}{\sqrt{3}} \right), \left(\tfrac{1}{\sqrt{2}}, 0, -\tfrac{1}{\sqrt{2}} \right), \left(\tfrac{1}{\sqrt{6}}, -\tfrac{2}{\sqrt{6}}, \tfrac{1}{\sqrt{6}} \right) \right\}.$$

We use the eigenvectors in E to form the columns of the transition matrix:

$$\mathbf{P} = \begin{pmatrix} \tfrac{1}{\sqrt{3}} & \tfrac{1}{\sqrt{2}} & \tfrac{1}{\sqrt{6}} \\ \tfrac{1}{\sqrt{3}} & 0 & -\tfrac{2}{\sqrt{6}} \\ \tfrac{1}{\sqrt{3}} & -\tfrac{1}{\sqrt{2}} & \tfrac{1}{\sqrt{6}} \end{pmatrix}.$$

We use the eigenvalues corresponding to the eigenvectors in E to form the diagonal matrix:

$$\mathbf{P}^T \mathbf{A} \mathbf{P} = \mathbf{D} = \begin{pmatrix} 8 & 0 & 0 \\ 0 & 2 & 0 \\ 0 & 0 & 2 \end{pmatrix}. \quad \blacksquare$$

Exercise 3.4   Orthogonally diagonalise the symmetric matrix

$$\mathbf{A} = \begin{pmatrix} 1 & 0 & 0 \\ 0 & 2 & 1 \\ 0 & 1 & 2 \end{pmatrix}.$$

You found the eigenvalues and eigenvectors of $\mathbf{A}$ in Exercise 2.9.

We end this subsection by proving Theorem 3.1.

Theorem 3.1 Eigenvectors corresponding to distinct eigenvalues of a symmetric matrix are orthogonal.

Proof   Let $\mathbf{A}$ be a symmetric matrix, and let $\mathbf{v}$ and $\mathbf{w}$ be eigenvectors of $\mathbf{A}$ corresponding to the distinct eigenvalues λ and μ. Then

$$\mathbf{A}\mathbf{v} = \lambda\mathbf{v} \quad \text{and} \quad \mathbf{A}\mathbf{w} = \mu\mathbf{w}.$$

To show that $\mathbf{v}$ and $\mathbf{w}$ are orthogonal, that is, $\mathbf{v} \cdot \mathbf{w} = 0$, we write $\mathbf{v}^T \mathbf{A} \mathbf{w}$ in two ways.

First,

$$\mathbf{v}^T \mathbf{A} \mathbf{w} = \mathbf{v}^T (\mathbf{A}\mathbf{w}) = \mathbf{v}^T (\mu\mathbf{w}) = \mu(\mathbf{v}^T \mathbf{w}) = \mu(\mathbf{v} \cdot \mathbf{w}).$$

Secondly, $\mathbf{A}$ is symmetric, so $\mathbf{A}^T = \mathbf{A}$; thus $\mathbf{v}^T \mathbf{A} = \mathbf{v}^T \mathbf{A}^T = (\mathbf{A}\mathbf{v})^T$. It follows that

$$\mathbf{v}^T \mathbf{A} \mathbf{w} = (\mathbf{v}^T \mathbf{A})\mathbf{w} = (\mathbf{A}\mathbf{v})^T \mathbf{w} = (\lambda\mathbf{v})^T \mathbf{w} = \lambda(\mathbf{v}^T \mathbf{w}) = \lambda(\mathbf{v} \cdot \mathbf{w}).$$

Note that $\mathbf{v}^T \mathbf{w} = \mathbf{v} \cdot \mathbf{w}$:

35

Since $\mathbf{v}^T(\mathbf{A}\mathbf{w}) = (\mathbf{v}^T\mathbf{A})\mathbf{w}$, we have $\lambda(\mathbf{v} \cdot \mathbf{w}) = \mu(\mathbf{v} \cdot \mathbf{w})$; thus

$$(\lambda - \mu)(\mathbf{v} \cdot \mathbf{w}) = 0.$$

Since the eigenvalues λ and μ are distinct, $\lambda - \mu$ is non-zero. Thus $\mathbf{v} \cdot \mathbf{w} = 0$, as required.   ■

3.2 Orthogonal matrices

In this subsection we look at some properties of orthogonal matrices. We have said that whenever $\mathbf{P}$ is an orthogonal matrix $\mathbf{P}^T = \mathbf{P}^{-1}$. We now prove the following result.

Theorem 3.2   A square matrix $\mathbf{P}$ is orthogonal if and only if $\mathbf{P}^T = \mathbf{P}^{-1}$.

Proof   Earlier we showed that for a square matrix $\mathbf{P}$, we have $\mathbf{P}^T = \mathbf{P}^{-1}$ Unit LA2, Section 4. if and only if $\mathbf{P}^T\mathbf{P} = \mathbf{I}$.

Let the columns of the matrix $\mathbf{P}$ be the column vectors $\mathbf{x}_1, \mathbf{x}_2, \ldots, \mathbf{x}_n$. Then the rows of the matrix $\mathbf{P}^T$ are the row vectors $\mathbf{x}_1, \mathbf{x}_2, \ldots, \mathbf{x}_n$.

For each i and j, the (i, j)-entry of $\mathbf{P}^T\mathbf{P}$ is the dot product of the ith row of $\mathbf{P}^T$ and the jth column of $\mathbf{P}$; that is, $\mathbf{x}_i \cdot \mathbf{x}_j$.

So $\mathbf{P}^T\mathbf{P} = \mathbf{I}$ if and only if

$$\mathbf{x}_i \cdot \mathbf{x}_j = 0 \text{ whenever } i \neq j \quad \text{and} \quad \mathbf{x}_i \cdot \mathbf{x}_i = 1 \text{ for each } i.$$

This is the case precisely when $\{\mathbf{x}_1, \ldots, \mathbf{x}_n\}$ is an orthonormal basis for $\mathbb{R}^n$; that is, when $\mathbf{P}$ is orthogonal.   ■

Several properties of orthogonal matrices follow from Theorem 3.2.

Corollary to Theorem 3.2   Let $\mathbf{P}$ and $\mathbf{Q}$ be orthogonal $n \times n$ matrices. Then:

(a) $\mathbf{P}^{-1}(= \mathbf{P}^T)$ is orthogonal;

(b) the rows of $\mathbf{P}$ form an orthonormal basis for $\mathbb{R}^n$;

(c) $\det \mathbf{P} = \pm 1$;

(d) the product $\mathbf{P}\mathbf{Q}$ is orthogonal.

Proof

(a) By Theorem 3.2, we have $\mathbf{P}^T = \mathbf{P}^{-1}$. Now,

$$(\mathbf{P}^{-1})^T\mathbf{P}^{-1} = (\mathbf{P}^T)^T\mathbf{P}^{-1} = \mathbf{P}\mathbf{P}^{-1} = \mathbf{I}.$$

Thus $(\mathbf{P}^{-1})^T = (\mathbf{P}^{-1})^{-1}$, so $\mathbf{P}^{-1}(= \mathbf{P}^T)$ is orthogonal.

(b) The rows of $\mathbf{P}$ are the columns of $\mathbf{P}^T$. The matrix $\mathbf{P}^T$ is orthogonal, by part (a), so its columns form an orthonormal basis for $\mathbb{R}^n$. Thus the rows of $\mathbf{P}$ form an orthonormal basis for $\mathbb{R}^n$.

(c) We know that $\det \mathbf{P}^T = \det \mathbf{P}$, and $\mathbf{P}^T\mathbf{P} = \mathbf{I}$, by Theorem 3.2. Now,

$$1 = \det \mathbf{I} = \det(\mathbf{P}^T\mathbf{P}) = (\det \mathbf{P}^T)(\det \mathbf{P}) = (\det \mathbf{P})^2.$$

Hence $\det \mathbf{P} = \pm 1$.

(d) The proof of this is left for you to do in Exercise 3.5. ■

Exercise 3.5　Prove part (d) of the corollary to Theorem 3.2.

To what transformations of the plane do 2×2 orthogonal matrices correspond? Suppose that

$$\mathbf{P} = \begin{pmatrix} a & b \\ c & d \end{pmatrix}$$

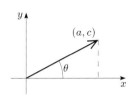

is an orthogonal matrix. Then the vectors (a, c) and (b, d) form an orthonormal basis for $\mathbb{R}^2$.

Let θ be the angle that the unit vector (a, c) makes with the x-axis, so

$$(a, c) = (\cos \theta, \sin \theta).$$

Since the unit vector (b, d) is orthogonal to (a, c), we have

$$(b, d) = (-\sin \theta, \cos \theta) \quad \text{or} \quad (\sin \theta, -\cos \theta).$$

Hence, if $\det \mathbf{P} = +1$, then

$$\mathbf{P} = \begin{pmatrix} \cos \theta & -\sin \theta \\ \sin \theta & \cos \theta \end{pmatrix},$$

and if $\det \mathbf{P} = -1$, then

$$\mathbf{P} = \begin{pmatrix} \cos \theta & \sin \theta \\ \sin \theta & -\cos \theta \end{pmatrix}.$$

Now suppose that $E = \{\mathbf{e}_1, \mathbf{e}_2\}$ is an orthonormal basis for $\mathbb{R}^2$ and that $\mathbf{P}$ is the orthogonal transition matrix whose columns are formed from the coordinates of $\mathbf{e}_1$ and $\mathbf{e}_2$.

We have just seen that if $\det \mathbf{P} = +1$, then

$$\mathbf{e}_1 = (\cos \theta, \sin \theta) \quad \text{and} \quad \mathbf{e}_2 = (-\sin \theta, \cos \theta),$$

that is, $\mathbf{e}_1$ and $\mathbf{e}_2$ are the images of the standard basis vectors $(1, 0)$ and $(0, 1)$ under a rotation r_θ.

Similarly, if $\det \mathbf{P} = -1$, then $\mathbf{e}_1$ and $\mathbf{e}_2$ are the images of the standard basis vectors $(1, 0)$ and $(0, 1)$ under a reflection $q_{\theta/2}$.

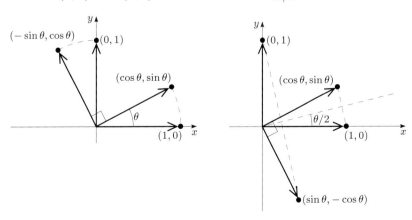

So if a 2×2 orthogonal matrix $\mathbf{P}$ is used to represent a linear transformation (as opposed to a transition matrix), then the linear transformation must be either a rotation or a reflection.

Similar arguments can be applied to 3×3 orthogonal matrices to show that linear transformations of $\mathbb{R}^3$ whose matrices are orthogonal are rotations about a line through the origin, reflections in a plane through the origin or combinations of these. The orthogonal matrices representing rotations of $\mathbb{R}^3$ are precisely those with determinant $+1$.

Exercise 3.6   Consider the matrix
$$\mathbf{A} = \begin{pmatrix} 0 & 0 & -1 \\ 0 & 1 & 0 \\ 1 & 0 & 0 \end{pmatrix}.$$

(a) Verify that this matrix is orthogonal.

(b) Show that this matrix represents a rotation of $\mathbb{R}^3$.

Further exercises

Exercise 3.7   Orthogonally diagonalise the matrix
$$\mathbf{A} = \begin{pmatrix} 5 & -1 \\ -1 & 5 \end{pmatrix}.$$

Exercise 3.8   Orthogonally diagonalise the matrix
$$\mathbf{A} = \begin{pmatrix} 0 & 1 & 0 \\ 1 & 0 & 0 \\ 0 & 0 & 0 \end{pmatrix}.$$

Exercise 3.9   Orthogonally diagonalise the matrix
$$\mathbf{A} = \begin{pmatrix} 1 & -4 & 2 \\ -4 & 1 & -2 \\ 2 & -2 & -2 \end{pmatrix}.$$

Exercise 3.10   Consider the matrix
$$\mathbf{A} = \begin{pmatrix} \frac{2}{7} & \frac{6}{7} & -\frac{3}{7} \\ -\frac{6}{7} & \frac{3}{7} & \frac{2}{7} \\ \frac{3}{7} & \frac{2}{7} & \frac{6}{7} \end{pmatrix}.$$

(a) Show that $\mathbf{A}$ is orthogonal.

(b) Write down $\mathbf{A}^{-1}$.

(c) Show that $\mathbf{A}$ represents a rotation of $\mathbb{R}^3$.

4   Conics and quadrics

After working through this section, you should be able to:

(a) write a given non-degenerate conic in standard form and classify it;

(b) understand the term *quadric* and recognise the six types of non-degenerate quadric;

(c) write a given non-degenerate quadric in standard form and classify it.

4.1 Classifying conics

Recall that a conic in $\mathbb{R}^2$ is the set of points (x, y) in $\mathbb{R}^2$ that satisfy an equation of the form

$$Ax^2 + Bxy + Cy^2 + Fx + Gy + H = 0, \tag{4.1}$$

where A, B and C are not all zero.

Unit LA1, Subsection 4.4.

There are three types of non-degenerate conic, as illustrated below.

We consider only non-degenerate conics.

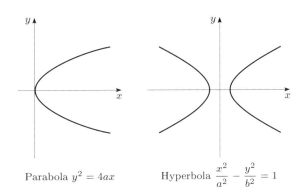

Ellipse $\dfrac{x^2}{a^2} + \dfrac{y^2}{b^2} = 1$ Parabola $y^2 = 4ax$ Hyperbola $\dfrac{x^2}{a^2} - \dfrac{y^2}{b^2} = 1$

The equations are in standard form, as above, only when the axes of the conic are parallel to the x-axis and y-axis, and the centre (if it has one) is at the origin. However, many of the equations of conics that arise in calculations are not in standard form; thus we need some way of determining the nature of a conic from its equation.

'Standard form' includes minor variations of these forms in which, for example, the roles of x and y are interchanged.

For example, the equation

$$x^2 - 4xy - 2y^2 + 6x + 12y + 21 = 0 \tag{4.2}$$

represents a conic in $\mathbb{R}^2$, as it has the same form as equation (4.1); but is the conic an ellipse, a parabola or a hyperbola? In this subsection we develop a technique for rewriting the equation of a given conic in standard form. We use the theory of the previous sections.

Equation (4.2) represents a hyperbola with centre $(1, 2)$, major axis $y = 2x$ and minor axis $x + 2y = 5$. This conic would be easily recognisable were we to *move the axes of the plane* so that they pass through the centre and line up with the major and minor axes of the conic. We can do this by rotating the page and translating it slightly to the right and up a bit, but how do we *move the plane* mathematically?

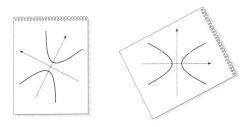

Introducing matrices

We first write equation (4.1) in matrix form as

$$\mathbf{x}^T \mathbf{A} \mathbf{x} + \mathbf{J}^T \mathbf{x} + H = 0, \qquad (4.3)$$

where

$$\mathbf{A} = \begin{pmatrix} A & \frac{1}{2}B \\ \frac{1}{2}B & C \end{pmatrix}, \quad \mathbf{J} = \begin{pmatrix} F \\ G \end{pmatrix}, \quad \mathbf{x} = \begin{pmatrix} x \\ y \end{pmatrix}.$$

Notice that the matrix $\mathbf{A}$ is symmetric.

This is possible, since

$$\mathbf{x}^T \mathbf{A} \mathbf{x} = \begin{pmatrix} x & y \end{pmatrix} \begin{pmatrix} A & \frac{1}{2}B \\ \frac{1}{2}B & C \end{pmatrix} \begin{pmatrix} x \\ y \end{pmatrix}$$

$$= \begin{pmatrix} x & y \end{pmatrix} \begin{pmatrix} Ax + \frac{1}{2}By \\ \frac{1}{2}Bx + Cy \end{pmatrix}$$

$$= Ax^2 + Bxy + Cy^2$$

and

$$\mathbf{J}^T \mathbf{x} = \begin{pmatrix} F & G \end{pmatrix} \begin{pmatrix} x \\ y \end{pmatrix}$$

$$= Fx + Gy.$$

For example, the conic with equation (4.2) can be written in matrix form (4.3) with

$$\mathbf{A} = \begin{pmatrix} 1 & -2 \\ -2 & -2 \end{pmatrix}, \quad \mathbf{J} = \begin{pmatrix} 6 \\ 12 \end{pmatrix}, \quad \mathbf{x} = \begin{pmatrix} x \\ y \end{pmatrix}, \quad H = 21.$$

Exercise 4.1   Write the equation of each of the following conics in matrix form:

(a) the ellipse $\dfrac{x^2}{a^2} + \dfrac{y^2}{b^2} = 1$;

(b) the hyperbola $\dfrac{x^2}{a^2} - \dfrac{y^2}{b^2} = 1$;

(c) the parabola $y^2 = 4ax$.

Aligning the axes

Next we see now how the matrix representation (4.3) helps us to recognise a conic. We can eliminate any xy-term from the equation of the conic by performing orthogonal diagonalisation on the symmetric matrix $\mathbf{A}$. Let the corresponding orthogonal transition matrix be $\mathbf{P}$. Then the columns of $\mathbf{P}$ form an orthonormal basis E, and $\mathbf{P}$ changes E-coordinates $\mathbf{x}_E$, which we shall write in the form $\mathbf{x}' = (x', y')$, into standard coordinates $\mathbf{x} = (x, y)$, that is, $\mathbf{x} = \mathbf{P}\mathbf{x}'$.

Then equation (4.3) becomes

$$(\mathbf{P}\mathbf{x}')^T \mathbf{A}(\mathbf{P}\mathbf{x}') + \mathbf{J}^T \mathbf{P}\mathbf{x}' + H = 0,$$

which can be rewritten as

$$(\mathbf{x}')^T (\mathbf{P}^T \mathbf{A}\mathbf{P})\mathbf{x}' + \mathbf{J}^T \mathbf{P}\mathbf{x}' + H = 0. \qquad (4.4)$$

Since $\mathbf{P}^T \mathbf{A}\mathbf{P} = \mathbf{D}$ is diagonal, there is no $x'y'$-term in the new equation for the conic, so its form more closely resembles the standard types given in the diagram on page 39.

Remark When choosing the orthonormal basis E, it is sometimes preferable for it to be a rotation (rather than a reflection) of the standard basis vectors. This is achieved either by geometric insight, or by ensuring that $\det \mathbf{P} = +1$.

We now illustrate this process by applying it to equation (4.2), where

$$\mathbf{A} = \begin{pmatrix} 1 & -2 \\ -2 & -2 \end{pmatrix}.$$

To orthogonally diagonalise $\mathbf{A}$, we use Strategy 3.1.

The eigenvalues of $\mathbf{A}$ are $\lambda = -3$ and $\lambda = 2$.

The eigenvectors of $\mathbf{A}$ are the non-zero vectors of the forms

$(k, 2k)$, corresponding to $\lambda = -3$,

and

$(-2k, k)$, corresponding to $\lambda = 2$.

It follows from Theorem 3.1 that we can form an orthonormal eigenvector basis of $\mathbf{A}$ by taking an eigenvector of unit length corresponding to each of the two distinct eigenvalues. For example,

$$E = \left\{ \left(\tfrac{1}{\sqrt{5}}, \tfrac{2}{\sqrt{5}} \right), \left(-\tfrac{2}{\sqrt{5}}, \tfrac{1}{\sqrt{5}} \right) \right\}$$

is an orthonormal eigenvector basis of $\mathbf{A}$.

We use the eigenvectors in E to form the columns of the transition matrix:

$$\mathbf{P} = \begin{pmatrix} \frac{1}{\sqrt{5}} & -\frac{2}{\sqrt{5}} \\ \frac{2}{\sqrt{5}} & \frac{1}{\sqrt{5}} \end{pmatrix}.$$

Note that $\det \mathbf{P} = +1$, so the basis vectors in E are the images of the standard basis vectors under a rotation.

We use the eigenvalues to form the diagonal matrix

$$\mathbf{P}^T \mathbf{A} \mathbf{P} = \mathbf{D} = \begin{pmatrix} -3 & 0 \\ 0 & 2 \end{pmatrix}.$$

It follows from equation (4.4) that the equation of the conic is now

$$\begin{pmatrix} x' & y' \end{pmatrix} \begin{pmatrix} -3 & 0 \\ 0 & 2 \end{pmatrix} \begin{pmatrix} x' \\ y' \end{pmatrix} + \begin{pmatrix} 6 & 12 \end{pmatrix} \begin{pmatrix} \frac{1}{\sqrt{5}} & -\frac{2}{\sqrt{5}} \\ \frac{2}{\sqrt{5}} & \frac{1}{\sqrt{5}} \end{pmatrix} \begin{pmatrix} x' \\ y' \end{pmatrix} + 21 = 0,$$

that is,

$$-3(x')^2 + 2(y')^2 + 6\sqrt{5}\,x' + 21 = 0.$$

In general, if

$$\mathbf{D} = \begin{pmatrix} \lambda_1 & 0 \\ 0 & \lambda_2 \end{pmatrix},$$

then equation (4.4) is of the form

$$\lambda_1 (x')^2 + \lambda_2 (y')^2 + f x' + g y' + H = 0, \tag{4.5}$$

where $\begin{pmatrix} f & g \end{pmatrix} = \mathbf{J}^T \mathbf{P}$.

You found these eigenvalues and eigenvectors in Exercise 1.5(b).

Translating the origin

To write the equation of the conic in standard form, we need also to eliminate the linear x' and y' terms corresponding to non-zero eigenvalues. This is achieved by moving the origin using a translation of the plane. To do this, we first *complete the squares* in the equation of the conic. For our example,

$$-3(x')^2 + 2(y')^2 + 6\sqrt{5}x' + 21 = 0$$

is equivalent to

$$-3((x')^2 - 2\sqrt{5}x') + 2(y')^2 + 21 = 0,$$

which can be written as

$$-3(x' - \sqrt{5})^2 + 15 + 2(y')^2 + 21 = 0,$$

or

$$-3(x' - \sqrt{5})^2 + 2(y')^2 + 36 = 0.$$

Here there is no linear y' term, so we need complete only the square involving x'.

To simplify further, we substitute $x'' = x' - \sqrt{5}$, $y'' = y'$, which results in the new coordinates $\mathbf{x}'' = (x'', y'') = (x' - \sqrt{5}, y')$. The equation of the conic is now

$$-3(x'')^2 + 2(y'')^2 = -36,$$

or

$$\frac{(x'')^2}{12} - \frac{(y'')^2}{18} = 1.$$

This equation is now recognisable as the equation of a hyperbola in standard form.

In general, if neither eigenvalue is 0, then equation (4.5) has the form

$$\lambda_1\left(x' + \frac{f}{2\lambda_1}\right)^2 - \lambda_1\left(\frac{f}{2\lambda_1}\right)^2 + \lambda_2\left(y' + \frac{g}{2\lambda_2}\right)^2 - \lambda_2\left(\frac{g}{2\lambda_2}\right)^2 + H = 0,$$

which can be written as

$$\lambda_1(x'')^2 + \lambda_2(y'')^2 = K,$$

where

$$x'' = x' + \frac{f}{2\lambda_1}, \quad y'' = y' + \frac{g}{2\lambda_2} \quad \text{and} \quad K = \frac{f^2}{4\lambda_1} + \frac{g^2}{4\lambda_2} - H.$$

If λ_1 (say) is 0 and $\lambda_2 \neq 0$, then equation (4.5) has the form

$$fx' + \lambda_2\left(y' + \frac{g}{2\lambda_2}\right)^2 - \lambda_2\left(\frac{g}{2\lambda_2}\right)^2 + H = 0;$$

that is, $\lambda_2(y'')^2 + fx'' = 0$, where

$$y'' = y' + \frac{g}{2\lambda_2}, \quad x'' = x' - \frac{\lambda_2}{f}\left(\frac{g}{2\lambda_2}\right)^2 + \frac{H}{f},$$

which is the equation of a parabola.

We summarise this method in the following strategy.

Strategy 4.1   To write the conic with equation

$$Ax^2 + Bxy + Cy^2 + Fx + Gy + H = 0$$

in standard form.

1. Introduce matrices.
    Write down the matrices $\mathbf{A} = \begin{pmatrix} A & \frac{1}{2}B \\ \frac{1}{2}B & C \end{pmatrix}$ and $\mathbf{J} = \begin{pmatrix} F \\ G \end{pmatrix}$.

2. Align the axes.
    (a) Orthogonally diagonalise $\mathbf{A}$:

    $$\mathbf{P}^T\mathbf{A}\mathbf{P} = \begin{pmatrix} \lambda_1 & 0 \\ 0 & \lambda_2 \end{pmatrix}.$$

    (b) Find $\begin{pmatrix} f & g \end{pmatrix} = \mathbf{J}^T\mathbf{P}$, and write the conic in the form

    $$\lambda_1(x')^2 + \lambda_2(y')^2 + fx' + gy' + H = 0. \tag{4.6}$$

3. Translate the origin.
    Complete the squares in equation (4.6), and change to the coordinate system (x'', y'').

If $\lambda_1, \lambda_2 \neq 0$, then (x'', y'')
$= \left(x' + \dfrac{f}{2\lambda_1}, y' + \dfrac{g}{2\lambda_2} \right).$

We illustrate Strategy 4.1 with the following example.

Example 4.1   Use Strategy 4.1 to write the conic with equation

$$5x^2 + 4xy + 5y^2 + 20x + 8y - 1 = 0$$

in standard form. Is this conic an ellipse, a parabola or a hyperbola?

Solution   Introduce matrices. We have

$$\mathbf{A} = \begin{pmatrix} 5 & 2 \\ 2 & 5 \end{pmatrix} \quad \text{and} \quad \mathbf{J} = \begin{pmatrix} 20 \\ 8 \end{pmatrix}.$$

Align the axes. We have

$$\mathbf{P}^T\mathbf{A}\mathbf{P} = \begin{pmatrix} 7 & 0 \\ 0 & 3 \end{pmatrix},$$

We orthogonally diagonalised $\mathbf{A}$ in Example 3.1.

where

$$\mathbf{P} = \begin{pmatrix} \frac{1}{\sqrt{2}} & -\frac{1}{\sqrt{2}} \\ \frac{1}{\sqrt{2}} & \frac{1}{\sqrt{2}} \end{pmatrix},$$

so

$$\begin{aligned} \begin{pmatrix} f & g \end{pmatrix} &= \begin{pmatrix} 20 & 8 \end{pmatrix} \begin{pmatrix} \frac{1}{\sqrt{2}} & -\frac{1}{\sqrt{2}} \\ \frac{1}{\sqrt{2}} & \frac{1}{\sqrt{2}} \end{pmatrix} \\ &= \begin{pmatrix} \frac{28}{\sqrt{2}} & -\frac{12}{\sqrt{2}} \end{pmatrix} \\ &= \begin{pmatrix} 14\sqrt{2} & -6\sqrt{2} \end{pmatrix}. \end{aligned}$$

The equation of the conic is now

$$7(x')^2 + 3(y')^2 + 14\sqrt{2}x' - 6\sqrt{2}y' - 1 = 0.$$

Translate the origin. We write this equation as

$$7((x')^2 + 2\sqrt{2}x') + 3((y')^2 - 2\sqrt{2}y') - 1 = 0.$$

Completing the squares in this equation, we obtain

$$7(x' + \sqrt{2})^2 - 14 + 3(y' - \sqrt{2})^2 - 6 - 1 = 0.$$

Simplifying this equation and substituting $x'' = x' + \sqrt{2}$ and $y'' = y' - \sqrt{2}$, we obtain

$$7(x'')^2 + 3(y'')^2 - 21 = 0.$$

The equation of the conic in standard form is

$$\frac{(x'')^2}{3} + \frac{(y'')^2}{7} = 1.$$

The conic is an ellipse. ∎

Exercise 4.2   Use Strategy 4.1 to write the conic with equation

$$x^2 - 4xy + 4y^2 - 6x - 8y + 5 = 0$$

in standard form. Is the conic an ellipse, a parabola or a hyperbola?

Exercise 4.3   Use Strategy 4.1 to write the conic with equation

$$9x^2 - 4xy + 6y^2 - 10x - 20y - 5 = 0$$

in standard form. Is the conic an ellipse, a parabola or a hyperbola?

Make use of the solution to Exercise 3.3(a).

4.2 Classifying quadrics

Quadrics are surfaces in $\mathbb{R}^3$. They are the three-dimensional analogues of conics.

Quadrics are often called *quadric surfaces*.

> **Definition**   A **quadric** in $\mathbb{R}^3$ is the set of points (x, y, z) that satisfy an equation of the form
>
> $$Ax^2 + By^2 + Cz^2 + Fxy + Gyz + Hxz + Jx + Ky + Lz + M = 0,$$
>
> where A, B, C, F, G and H are not all 0.

There are six types of non-degenerate quadric. These are illustrated below, with a typical equation for each in standard form. In each case, we state also the curve of intersection of a plane parallel to a coordinate plane that meets the quadric in a non-trivial intersection—these intersections help us to identify the quadrics.

As with conics, 'standard form' includes minor variations of the forms given here.

Ellipsoid $\dfrac{x^2}{l^2} + \dfrac{y^2}{m^2} + \dfrac{z^2}{n^2} = 1$

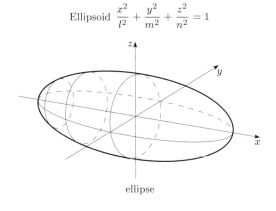

ellipse

Elliptic cone $z^2 = \dfrac{x^2}{l^2} + \dfrac{y^2}{m^2}$

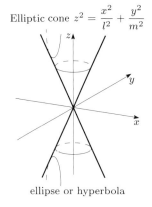

ellipse or hyperbola

Hyperboloid $\dfrac{x^2}{l^2} + \dfrac{y^2}{m^2} - \dfrac{z^2}{n^2} = 1$
of one sheet

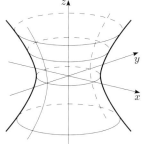

ellipse or hyperbola

Elliptic paraboloid $z = \dfrac{x^2}{l^2} + \dfrac{y^2}{m^2}$

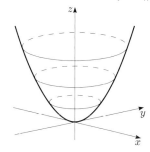

ellipse or parabola

Hyperboloid $\dfrac{x^2}{l^2} + \dfrac{y^2}{m^2} - \dfrac{z^2}{n^2} = -1$
of two sheets

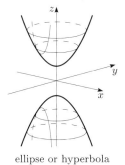

ellipse or hyperbola

Hyperbolic paraboloid $z = \dfrac{x^2}{l^2} - \dfrac{y^2}{m^2}$

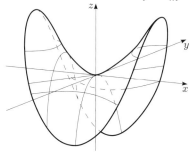

hyperbola or parabola

To write the equation of a quadric in standard form, we use the same techniques that we used for conics: introduce matrices, align the axes (orthogonal diagonalisation) and translate the origin.

We summarise this method in the following strategy.

We omit the justification—it is analogous to that for conics.

Strategy 4.2   To write the quadric with equation

$$Ax^2 + By^2 + Cz^2 + Fxy + Gyz + Hxz + Jx + Ky + Lz + M = 0$$

in standard form.

1. Introduce matrices.

   Write down the matrices

   $$\mathbf{A} = \begin{pmatrix} A & \tfrac{1}{2}F & \tfrac{1}{2}H \\ \tfrac{1}{2}F & B & \tfrac{1}{2}G \\ \tfrac{1}{2}H & \tfrac{1}{2}G & C \end{pmatrix} \quad \text{and} \quad \mathbf{J} = \begin{pmatrix} J \\ K \\ L \end{pmatrix}.$$

2. Align the axes.

   (a) Orthogonally diagonalise $\mathbf{A}$:

   $$\mathbf{P}^T \mathbf{A} \mathbf{P} = \begin{pmatrix} \lambda_1 & 0 & 0 \\ 0 & \lambda_2 & 0 \\ 0 & 0 & \lambda_3 \end{pmatrix}.$$

   (b) Find $\begin{pmatrix} f & g & h \end{pmatrix} = \mathbf{J}^T \mathbf{P}$, and write the quadric in the form

   $$\lambda_1 (x')^2 + \lambda_2 (y')^2 + \lambda_3 (z')^2 + fx' + gy' + hz' + M = 0. \qquad (4.7)$$

3. Translate the origin.

   Complete the squares in equation (4.7), and change to the coordinate system (x'', y'', z'').

If $\lambda_1, \lambda_2, \lambda_3 \neq 0$, then
$$(x'', y'', z'')$$
$$= \left(x' + \frac{f}{2\lambda_1}, y' + \frac{g}{2\lambda_2}, z' + \frac{h}{2\lambda_3} \right).$$

We illustrate Strategy 4.2 with the following example.

Example 4.2   Use Strategy 4.2 to write the quadric with equation

$$5x^2 + 3y^2 + 3z^2 - 2xy + 2yz - 2xz - 10x + 6y - 2z - 9 = 0$$

in standard form. Which of the six types of non-degenerate quadric does this represent?

Solution   Introduce matrices. We have

$$\mathbf{A} = \begin{pmatrix} 5 & -1 & -1 \\ -1 & 3 & 1 \\ -1 & 1 & 3 \end{pmatrix}, \quad \mathbf{J} = \begin{pmatrix} -10 \\ 6 \\ -2 \end{pmatrix}, \quad \mathbf{x} = \begin{pmatrix} x \\ y \\ z \end{pmatrix}.$$

Align the axes. We have

$$\mathbf{P}^T \mathbf{A} \mathbf{P} = \begin{pmatrix} 6 & 0 & 0 \\ 0 & 3 & 0 \\ 0 & 0 & 2 \end{pmatrix},$$

where

$$\mathbf{P} = \begin{pmatrix} -\frac{2}{\sqrt{6}} & \frac{1}{\sqrt{3}} & 0 \\ \frac{1}{\sqrt{6}} & \frac{1}{\sqrt{3}} & \frac{1}{\sqrt{2}} \\ \frac{1}{\sqrt{6}} & \frac{1}{\sqrt{3}} & -\frac{1}{\sqrt{2}} \end{pmatrix}.$$

> You orthogonally diagonalised $\mathbf{A}$ in Exercise 3.3(b).

> Since $\det \mathbf{P} = 1$, this transition matrix represents a rotation of the basis vectors.

So

$$\begin{pmatrix} f & g & h \end{pmatrix} = \begin{pmatrix} -10 & 6 & -2 \end{pmatrix} \begin{pmatrix} -\frac{2}{\sqrt{6}} & \frac{1}{\sqrt{3}} & 0 \\ \frac{1}{\sqrt{6}} & \frac{1}{\sqrt{3}} & \frac{1}{\sqrt{2}} \\ \frac{1}{\sqrt{6}} & \frac{1}{\sqrt{3}} & -\frac{1}{\sqrt{2}} \end{pmatrix}$$

$$= \begin{pmatrix} 4\sqrt{6} & -2\sqrt{3} & 4\sqrt{2} \end{pmatrix}.$$

The equation of the quadric is now

$$6(x')^2 + 3(y')^2 + 2(z')^2 + 4\sqrt{6}x' - 2\sqrt{3}y' + 4\sqrt{2}z' - 9 = 0.$$

Translate the origin. Completing the squares in this equation, we obtain

$$6\left(x' + \tfrac{2}{\sqrt{6}}\right)^2 - 4 + 3\left(y' - \tfrac{1}{\sqrt{3}}\right)^2 - 1 + 2(z' + \sqrt{2})^2 - 4 - 9 = 0.$$

Simplifying this equation and substituting $x'' = x' + \frac{2}{\sqrt{6}}$, $y'' = y' - \frac{1}{\sqrt{3}}$ and $z'' = z' + \sqrt{2}$, we obtain

$$6(x'')^2 + 3(y'')^2 + 2(z'')^2 - 18 = 0.$$

The equation of the quadric in standard form is

$$\frac{(x'')^2}{3} + \frac{(y'')^2}{6} + \frac{(z'')^2}{9} = 1.$$

This is the equation of an ellipsoid.   ∎

> **Exercise 4.4**   Use Strategy 4.2 to write the quadric with equation
>
> $$x^2 + y^2 + z^2 - 2x + 4y - 6z - 11 = 0$$
>
> in standard form. Which of the six types of non-degenerate quadric does this represent?

> **Exercise 4.5**   Use Strategy 4.2 to write the quadric with equation
>
> $$4x^2 + 3y^2 + 2z^2 + 4xy + 4yz + 12x + 12z + 18 = 0$$
>
> in standard form. Which of the six types of non-degenerate quadric does this represent?

> We orthogonally diagonalised the matrix $\mathbf{A}$ of this quadric on page 31.

Further exercises

Exercise 4.6   Write the conic with equation

$$x^2 - 2y^2 - 4x - 12y - 18 = 0$$

in standard form. Is this conic an ellipse, a parabola or a hyperbola?

Exercise 4.7   Use the solution to Exercise 3.7 to write the conic with equation

$$5x^2 - 2xy + 5y^2 - 1 = 0$$

in standard form. Is this conic an ellipse, a parabola or a hyperbola?

Exercise 4.8   Use the solution to Exercise 3.8 to write the quadric with equation

$$2xy - 6x + 10y + z - 30 = 0$$

in standard form. Which of the six types of non-degenerate quadric does this equation represent?

Exercise 4.9   Write the quadric with equation

$$x^2 + y^2 + x - z = 0$$

in standard form. Which of the six types of non-degenerate quadric does this equation represent?

Exercise 4.10   Write the quadric with equation

$$2xy + z = 0$$

in standard form. Which of the six types of non-degenerate quadric does this equation represent?

Solutions to the exercises

1.1 We have
$$t(2,-2) = (2-8, 2+4) = (-6, 6)$$
$$= -3(2, -2)$$
and
$$t(-7, 7) = (-7+28, -7-14) = (21, -21)$$
$$= -3(-7, 7).$$
In each case the original vector is scaled by the factor -3.

1.2 (a) We have $t(0,1) = (4, -2)$, $t(1, 2) = (9, -3)$ and $t(4, 1) = (8, 2)$.

(b) The linear transformation t maps the line joining the points $(0, 0)$ and $(4, 1)$ to the line joining the points $(0, 0)$ and $(8, 2)$. But $(8, 2) = 2(4, 1)$, so these lines are the same and both can be written as $x = 4y$. Therefore the line $x = 4y$ is mapped to itself by the linear transformation t.

(c) We have
$$t(4k, k) = (4k + 4k, 4k - 2k) = (8k, 2k)$$
$$= 2(4k, k),$$
so any vector lying along the line $x = 4y$ is scaled by the factor 2.

1.3 (a) A reflection t in the line $y = x$ maps the point (x, y) to the point (y, x). Each point on the line $y = x$ is mapped to itself, since
$$t(k, k) = (k, k) = 1(k, k),$$
so the non-zero vectors (k, k) are eigenvectors with corresponding eigenvalue 1.

Each point on the line $y = -x$ is mapped to another point on the line $y = -x$, since
$$t(k, -k) = (-k, k) = -1(k, -k),$$
so the non-zero vectors $(k, -k)$ are eigenvectors with corresponding eigenvalue -1.

(b) A 2-dilation t maps the point (x, y) to the point $(2x, 2y)$. Every line through the origin is mapped to itself; that is, every non-zero vector in the plane is an eigenvector of t. Let k and l be real numbers which are not both zero. Then
$$t(k, l) = (2k, 2l) = 2(k, l),$$
so the non-zero vectors (k, l) are eigenvectors with corresponding eigenvalue 2.

(c) An anticlockwise rotation t through $\pi/2$ maps the point (x, y) to the point $(-y, x)$. No line through the origin is mapped to itself by t, so t has no eigenvectors.

(d) An anticlockwise rotation t through π maps the point (x, y) to the point $(-x, -y)$. Each line through the origin is mapped to itself; that is, each non-zero vector in the plane is an eigenvector of t.

Let k and l be real numbers which are not both zero. Then
$$t(k, l) = (-k, -l) = -1(k, l),$$
so the non-zero vectors (k, l) are eigenvectors with corresponding eigenvalue -1.

1.4 (a) We wish to find those vectors (x, y) which are mapped to scalar multiples of themselves; that is, the vectors that satisfy
$$(-5x + 3y, 6x - 2y) = (\lambda x, \lambda y).$$
Comparing coordinates, we obtain the simultaneous equations
$$\begin{cases} -5x + 3y = \lambda x, \\ 6x - 2y = \lambda y, \end{cases}$$
which we write as
$$\begin{cases} (-5 - \lambda)x + 3y = 0, \\ 6x + (-2 - \lambda)y = 0. \end{cases}$$

(b) Non-zero solutions to the eigenvector equations exist if and only if the determinant of the coefficient matrix is 0; that is, if and only if
$$\begin{vmatrix} -5 - \lambda & 3 \\ 6 & -2 - \lambda \end{vmatrix} = 0.$$
We expand this determinant and obtain
$$(-5 - \lambda)(-2 - \lambda) - 18 = 0,$$
which simplifies (after some algebra) to
$$\lambda^2 + 7\lambda - 8 = 0.$$
The eigenvalues of t are the solutions to this characteristic equation. We have
$$\lambda^2 + 7\lambda - 8 = (\lambda - 1)(\lambda + 8) = 0,$$
so the eigenvalues are $\lambda = 1$ and $\lambda = -8$.

(c) To find the corresponding eigenvectors, we consider each value of λ in turn.

$\boxed{\lambda = 1}$ The eigenvector equations become
$$\begin{cases} -6x + 3y = 0, \\ 6x - 3y = 0. \end{cases}$$
These equations are equivalent to the single equation
$$2x - y = 0.$$
Thus the eigenvectors corresponding to $\lambda = 1$ are the non-zero vectors (x, y) for which $y = 2x$; that is, the vectors of the form
$$(k, 2k), \quad \text{where } k \neq 0.$$

$\boxed{\lambda = -8}$ The eigenvector equations become
$$\begin{cases} 3x + 3y = 0, \\ 6x + 6y = 0. \end{cases}$$
These equations are equivalent to the single equation
$$x + y = 0.$$

Thus the eigenvectors corresponding to $\lambda = -8$ are the non-zero vectors (x, y) for which $y = -x$; that is, the vectors of the form

$(k, -k)$,   where $k \neq 0$.

Thus the eigenvectors of t are the non-zero vectors of the forms

$(k, 2k)$, corresponding to $\lambda = 1$,

and

$(k, -k)$, corresponding to $\lambda = -8$.

1.5 **(a)** The matrix of t with respect to the standard basis for $\mathbb{R}^2$ is

$$\mathbf{A} = \begin{pmatrix} 1 & 3 \\ 2 & -4 \end{pmatrix}.$$

We use Strategy 1.1 to find the eigenvalues and eigenvectors of $\mathbf{A}$, which are the same as those of t.

First we find the eigenvalues of $\mathbf{A}$.

The characteristic equation of $\mathbf{A}$ is $\det(\mathbf{A} - \lambda\mathbf{I}) = 0$; that is,

$$\begin{vmatrix} 1 - \lambda & 3 \\ 2 & -4 - \lambda \end{vmatrix} = 0.$$

We expand this determinant and obtain

$(1 - \lambda)(-4 - \lambda) - 6 = 0,$

which simplifies to

$\lambda^2 + 3\lambda - 10 = (\lambda - 2)(\lambda + 5) = 0.$

The eigenvalues of $\mathbf{A}$ are therefore $\lambda = 2$ and $\lambda = -5$.

Next we find the eigenvectors of $\mathbf{A}$.

The eigenvector equations are

$$\begin{cases} (1 - \lambda)x + & 3y = 0, \\ 2x + (-4 - \lambda)y = 0. \end{cases}$$

$\boxed{\lambda = 2}$ The eigenvector equations become

$$\begin{cases} -x + 3y = 0, \\ 2x - 6y = 0. \end{cases}$$

These equations are equivalent to the single equation

$x - 3y = 0.$

Thus the eigenvectors corresponding to $\lambda = 2$ are the non-zero vectors for which $x = 3y$; that is, the vectors of the form

$(3k, k)$,   where $k \neq 0$.

$\boxed{\lambda = -5}$ The eigenvector equations become

$$\begin{cases} 6x + 3y = 0, \\ 2x + y = 0. \end{cases}$$

These equations are equivalent to the single equation

$2x + y = 0.$

Thus the eigenvectors corresponding to $\lambda = -5$ are the non-zero vectors for which $y = -2x$; that is, the vectors of the form

$(k, -2k)$,   where $k \neq 0$.

Thus the eigenvectors of t are the non-zero vectors of the forms

$(3k, k)$, corresponding to $\lambda = 2$,

and

$(k, -2k)$, corresponding to $\lambda = -5$.

(b) The matrix of t with respect to the standard basis for $\mathbb{R}^2$ is

$$\mathbf{A} = \begin{pmatrix} 1 & -2 \\ -2 & -2 \end{pmatrix}.$$

We use Strategy 1.1 to find the eigenvalues and eigenvectors of $\mathbf{A}$, which are the same as those of t.

First we find the eigenvalues of $\mathbf{A}$.

The characteristic equation of $\mathbf{A}$ is $\det(\mathbf{A} - \lambda\mathbf{I}) = 0$; that is,

$$\begin{vmatrix} 1 - \lambda & -2 \\ -2 & -2 - \lambda \end{vmatrix} = 0.$$

We expand this determinant and obtain

$(1 - \lambda)(-2 - \lambda) - 4 = 0,$

which simplifies to

$\lambda^2 + \lambda - 6 = (\lambda - 2)(\lambda + 3) = 0.$

The eigenvalues of $\mathbf{A}$ are therefore $\lambda = 2$ and $\lambda = -3$.

Next we find the eigenvectors of $\mathbf{A}$.

The eigenvector equations are

$$\begin{cases} (1 - \lambda)x - & 2y = 0, \\ -2x + (-2 - \lambda)y = 0. \end{cases}$$

$\boxed{\lambda = 2}$ The eigenvector equations become

$$\begin{cases} -x - 2y = 0, \\ -2x - 4y = 0. \end{cases}$$

These equations are equivalent to the single equation

$x + 2y = 0.$

Thus the eigenvectors corresponding to $\lambda = 2$ are the non-zero vectors for which $x = -2y$; that is, the vectors of the form

$(-2k, k)$,   where $k \neq 0$.

$\boxed{\lambda = -3}$ The eigenvector equations become

$$\begin{cases} 4x - 2y = 0, \\ -2x + y = 0. \end{cases}$$

These equations are equivalent to the single equation

$2x - y = 0.$

Thus the eigenvectors corresponding to $\lambda = -3$ are the non-zero vectors for which $y = 2x$; that is, the vectors of the form

$(k, 2k)$,   where $k \neq 0$.

Thus the eigenvectors of t are the non-zero vectors of the forms

$(-2k, k)$, corresponding to $\lambda = 2$,

and

$(k, 2k)$, corresponding to $\lambda = -3$.

1.6 The matrix of t with respect to the standard basis for $\mathbb{R}^3$ is

$$\mathbf{A} = \begin{pmatrix} 4 & 2 & 0 \\ 2 & 3 & 2 \\ 0 & 2 & 2 \end{pmatrix}.$$

We use Strategy 1.1 to find the eigenvalues and eigenvectors of $\mathbf{A}$, which are the same as those of t.

First we find the eigenvalues of $\mathbf{A}$.

The characteristic equation is $\det(\mathbf{A} - \lambda\mathbf{I}) = 0$; that is,

$$\begin{vmatrix} 4 - \lambda & 2 & 0 \\ 2 & 3 - \lambda & 2 \\ 0 & 2 & 2 - \lambda \end{vmatrix} = 0.$$

We expand this determinant and obtain

$$(4 - \lambda)\begin{vmatrix} 3 - \lambda & 2 \\ 2 & 2 - \lambda \end{vmatrix} - 2\begin{vmatrix} 2 & 2 \\ 0 & 2 - \lambda \end{vmatrix} + 0 = 0.$$

Simplifying this expression, we obtain

$$(4 - \lambda)((3 - \lambda)(2 - \lambda) - 4) - 2(2(2 - \lambda)) = 0,$$

or

$$\lambda^3 - 9\lambda^2 + 18\lambda = 0.$$

There is no constant term, so we take out the factor λ, then factorise the remaining quadratic factor:

$$\lambda(\lambda^2 - 9\lambda + 18) = \lambda(\lambda - 6)(\lambda - 3) = 0.$$

The eigenvalues of $\mathbf{A}$ are therefore $\lambda = 0$, $\lambda = 6$ and $\lambda = 3$.

Next we find the eigenvectors of $\mathbf{A}$.

The eigenvector equations are

$$\begin{cases} (4 - \lambda)x + & 2y & = 0, \\ 2x + (3 - \lambda)y + & 2z & = 0, \\ & 2y + (2 - \lambda)z & = 0. \end{cases}$$

$\boxed{\lambda = 6}$ The eigenvector equations become

$$\begin{cases} -2x + 2y & = 0, \\ 2x - 3y + 2z & = 0, \\ 2y - 4z & = 0. \end{cases}$$

The first and third equations imply that $x = y$ and $y = 2z$, so $x = 2z$. These satisfy the second equation. Thus the eigenvectors corresponding to the eigenvalue $\lambda = 6$ are the non-zero vectors (x, y, z) satisfying $y = 2z$ and $x = 2z$; that is, the vectors of the form

$(2k, 2k, k)$, where $k \neq 0$.

$\boxed{\lambda = 3}$ The eigenvector equations become

$$\begin{cases} x + 2y & = 0, \\ 2x & + 2z = 0, \\ 2y - & z = 0. \end{cases}$$

The first and second equations imply that $x = -2y$ and $z = -x$, so $z = 2y$. These satisfy the third equation. Thus the eigenvectors corresponding to the eigenvalue $\lambda = 3$ are the non-zero vectors (x, y, z) satisfying $x = -2y$ and $z = 2y$; that is, the vectors of the form

$(-2k, k, 2k)$, where $k \neq 0$.

$\boxed{\lambda = 0}$ The eigenvector equations become

$$\begin{cases} 4x + 2y & = 0, \\ 2x + 3y + 2z & = 0, \\ 2y + 2z & = 0. \end{cases}$$

The first and third equations imply that $y = -2x$ and $z = -y$, so $z = 2x$. These satisfy the second equation. Thus the eigenvectors corresponding to the eigenvalue $\lambda = 0$ are the non-zero vectors (x, y, z) satisfying $y = -2x$ and $z = 2x$; that is, the vectors of the form

$(k, -2k, 2k)$, where $k \neq 0$.

Thus the eigenvectors of t are the non-zero vectors of the forms

$(2k, 2k, k)$, corresponding to $\lambda = 6$,

$(-2k, k, 2k)$, corresponding to $\lambda = 3$,

and

$(k, -2k, 2k)$, corresponding to $\lambda = 0$.

1.7 (a) Let

$$\mathbf{A} = \begin{pmatrix} 1 & 2 \\ 0 & 6 \end{pmatrix}.$$

The characteristic equation is $\det(\mathbf{A} - \lambda\mathbf{I}) = 0$; that is,

$$\begin{vmatrix} 1 - \lambda & 2 \\ 0 & 6 - \lambda \end{vmatrix} = 0.$$

We expand this determinant and obtain

$$(1 - \lambda)(6 - \lambda) - 0 = 0.$$

The eigenvalues of $\mathbf{A}$ are therefore $\lambda = 1$ and $\lambda = 6$. Notice that these are the diagonal entries of the matrix $\mathbf{A}$.

(b) Let

$$\mathbf{A} = \begin{pmatrix} 8 & 0 & 0 \\ 0 & -5 & 0 \\ 0 & 0 & 21 \end{pmatrix}.$$

The characteristic equation is $\det(\mathbf{A} - \lambda\mathbf{I}) = 0$; that is,

$$\begin{vmatrix} 8 - \lambda & 0 & 0 \\ 0 & -5 - \lambda & 0 \\ 0 & 0 & 21 - \lambda \end{vmatrix} = 0.$$

We expand this determinant and obtain

$$(8 - \lambda)\begin{vmatrix} -5 - \lambda & 0 \\ 0 & 21 - \lambda \end{vmatrix} = 0.$$

Simplifying this expression, we obtain

$$(8 - \lambda)((-5 - \lambda)(21 - \lambda) - 0) = 0.$$

The eigenvalues of $\mathbf{A}$ are therefore $\lambda = 8$, $\lambda = -5$ and $\lambda = 21$. Again, these are the diagonal entries of the matrix $\mathbf{A}$.

(c) Let

$$\mathbf{A} = \begin{pmatrix} 4 & 0 & 0 \\ 25 & -2 & 0 \\ 17 & \pi & 6 \end{pmatrix}.$$

The characteristic equation is $\det(\mathbf{A} - \lambda\mathbf{I}) = 0$; that is,

$$\begin{vmatrix} 4 - \lambda & 0 & 0 \\ 25 & -2 - \lambda & 0 \\ 17 & \pi & 6 - \lambda \end{vmatrix} = 0.$$

We expand this determinant and obtain

$$(4 - \lambda)\begin{vmatrix} -2 - \lambda & 0 \\ \pi & 6 - \lambda \end{vmatrix} = 0.$$

Simplifying this expression, we obtain

$$(4 - \lambda)((-2 - \lambda)(6 - \lambda) - 0) = 0.$$

The eigenvalues of $\mathbf{A}$ are therefore $\lambda = 4$, $\lambda = -2$ and $\lambda = 6$. Again, these are the diagonal entries of the matrix $\mathbf{A}$.

1.8 $\boxed{\lambda = 6}$ The non-zero vectors of the form $(2k, 2k, k)$ are the eigenvectors of t corresponding to $\lambda = 6$. The eigenspace $S(6)$ is therefore the set of vectors

$$\{(2k, 2k, k) : k \in \mathbb{R}\}.$$

Any vector in $S(6)$ can be written as $k(2, 2, 1)$, so $\{(2, 2, 1)\}$ is a basis for $S(6)$.

Thus $S(6)$ has dimension 1.

$\boxed{\lambda = 3}$ The non-zero vectors of the form $(-2k, k, 2k)$ are the eigenvectors of t corresponding to $\lambda = 3$. The eigenspace $S(3)$ is therefore the set of vectors

$$\{(-2k, k, 2k) : k \in \mathbb{R}\}.$$

Any vector in $S(3)$ can be written as $k(-2, 1, 2)$, so $\{(-2, 1, 2)\}$ is a basis for $S(3)$.

Thus $S(3)$ has dimension 1.

1.9 Let

$$\mathbf{A} = \begin{pmatrix} 4 & 2 & 2 \\ 2 & 4 & 2 \\ 2 & 2 & 4 \end{pmatrix}.$$

The characteristic equation is $\det(\mathbf{A} - \lambda\mathbf{I}) = 0$; that is,

$$\begin{vmatrix} 4 - \lambda & 2 & 2 \\ 2 & 4 - \lambda & 2 \\ 2 & 2 & 4 - \lambda \end{vmatrix} = 0.$$

We expand this determinant and obtain

$$(4 - \lambda)\begin{vmatrix} 4 - \lambda & 2 \\ 2 & 4 - \lambda \end{vmatrix} - 2\begin{vmatrix} 2 & 2 \\ 2 & 4 - \lambda \end{vmatrix}$$
$$+ 2\begin{vmatrix} 2 & 4 - \lambda \\ 2 & 2 \end{vmatrix} = 0.$$

This simplifies to

$$-\lambda^3 + 12\lambda^2 - 36\lambda + 32$$
$$= -(\lambda - 8)(\lambda - 2)(\lambda - 2) = 0.$$

The eigenvalues of $\mathbf{A}$ are $\lambda = 8$, $\lambda = 2$ and $\lambda = 2$.

The eigenvector equations are

$$\begin{cases} (4 - \lambda)x + & 2y + & 2z = 0, \\ 2x + & (4 - \lambda)y + & 2z = 0, \\ 2x + & 2y + & (4 - \lambda)z = 0. \end{cases}$$

$\boxed{\lambda = 8}$ The eigenvalue $\lambda = 8$ has multiplicity 1.

The eigenvector equations become

$$\begin{cases} -4x + 2y + 2z = 0, \\ 2x - 4y + 2z = 0, \\ 2x + 2y - 4z = 0. \end{cases}$$

Taking the second equation from the first, we obtain $-6x + 6y = 0$, which implies that $x = y$. Substituting this into the third equation, we obtain $4x - 4z = 0$, which implies that $x = z$.

Thus the eigenvectors corresponding to the eigenvalue $\lambda = 8$ are the vectors of the form (k, k, k), where $k \neq 0$.

The eigenspace $S(8)$ is the set of vectors

$$\{(k, k, k) : k \in \mathbb{R}\}.$$

Any vector in $S(8)$ can be written as $k(1, 1, 1)$, so

$$\{(1, 1, 1)\}$$

is a basis for $S(8)$.

Thus $S(8)$ has dimension 1.

Geometrically, $S(8)$ is the line in $\mathbb{R}^3$ given by $x = y = z$.

$\boxed{\lambda = 2}$ The eigenvalue $\lambda = 2$ has multiplicity 2.

All three eigenvector equations become

$$2x + 2y + 2z = 0,$$

that is, $x + y + z = 0$, so $z = -(x + y)$.

Thus the eigenvectors corresponding to the eigenvalue $\lambda = 2$ are the vectors of the form $(k, l, -(k + l))$, where k and l are not both 0.

The eigenspace $S(2)$ is the set of vectors

$$\{(k, l, -(k + l)) : k, l \in \mathbb{R}\}.$$

Any vector in $S(2)$ can be written as $k(1, 0, -1) + l(0, 1, -1)$, so

$$\{(1, 0, -1), (0, 1, -1)\}$$

is a basis for $S(2)$.

Thus $S(2)$ has dimension 2.

Geometrically, $S(2)$ is the plane in $\mathbb{R}^3$ given by $x + y + z = 0$.

1.10 The matrix

$$\mathbf{A} = \begin{pmatrix} 1 & 1 \\ 0 & 1 \end{pmatrix}$$

is triangular, so the eigenvalues are the diagonal entries $\lambda = 1$ and $\lambda = 1$.

The eigenvector equations are

$$\begin{cases} (1 - \lambda)x + & y = 0, \\ & (1 - \lambda)y = 0. \end{cases}$$

$\boxed{\lambda = 1}$ The eigenvalue $\lambda = 1$ has multiplicity 2.

The eigenvector equations become

$$\begin{cases} 0x + & y = 0, \\ & 0y = 0. \end{cases}$$

Thus $y = 0$ and there are no constraints on x.

Thus the eigenvectors corresponding to the eigenvalue $\lambda = 1$ are the vectors of the form $(k, 0)$, where $k \neq 0$.

The eigenspace $S(1)$ is the set of vectors

$$\{(k, 0) : k \in \mathbb{R}\}.$$

Any vector in $S(1)$ can be written as $k(1, 0)$, so

$$\{(1, 0)\}$$

is a basis for $S(1)$.

Thus $S(1)$ has dimension 1.

Geometrically, $S(1)$ is the x-axis in $\mathbb{R}^2$.

1.11 Since $\mathbf{v}$ is an eigenvector of the linear transformation t with corresponding eigenvalue λ, we have

$$t(\mathbf{v}) = \lambda \mathbf{v}.$$

Let k be any non-zero number. Then

$$t(k\mathbf{v}) = k\, t(\mathbf{v}) = k(\lambda \mathbf{v}) = \lambda(k\mathbf{v}),$$

so $k\mathbf{v}$ is also an eigenvector of the linear transformation t with corresponding eigenvalue λ.

1.12 The matrix of t with respect to the standard basis for $\mathbb{R}^2$ is

$$\mathbf{A} = \begin{pmatrix} -5 & 3 \\ 6 & -2 \end{pmatrix}.$$

We use Strategy 1.1 to find the eigenvalues and eigenvectors of $\mathbf{A}$, which are the same as those of t.

First we find the eigenvalues of $\mathbf{A}$.

The characteristic equation of $\mathbf{A}$ is

$$\begin{vmatrix} -5 - \lambda & 3 \\ 6 & -2 - \lambda \end{vmatrix} = 0.$$

We expand this determinant and obtain

$$(-5 - \lambda)(-2 - \lambda) - 18 = 0,$$

which simplifies to

$$\lambda^2 + 7\lambda - 8 = (\lambda - 1)(\lambda + 8) = 0.$$

The eigenvalues of $\mathbf{A}$ are therefore $\lambda = 1$ and $\lambda = -8$.

Next we find the eigenvectors of $\mathbf{A}$.

The eigenvector equations are

$$\begin{cases} (-5 - \lambda)x + \; 3y = 0, \\ \; 6x + (-2 - \lambda)y = 0. \end{cases}$$

$\boxed{\lambda = 1}$ The eigenvector equations become

$$\begin{cases} -6x + 3y = 0, \\ 6x - 3y = 0. \end{cases}$$

These equations are equivalent to the single equation $2x - y = 0$. Thus the eigenvectors corresponding to $\lambda = 1$ are the non-zero vectors for which $y = 2x$; that is, the vectors of the form

$$(k, 2k), \quad \text{where } k \neq 0.$$

$\boxed{\lambda = -8}$ The eigenvector equations become

$$\begin{cases} 3x + 3y = 0, \\ 6x + 6y = 0. \end{cases}$$

These equations are equivalent to the single equation $x + y = 0$.

Thus the eigenvectors corresponding to $\lambda = -8$ are the non-zero vectors for which $y = -x$; that is, the vectors of the form

$$(k, -k), \quad \text{where } k \neq 0.$$

Thus the eigenvectors of the linear transformation t are the non-zero vectors of the forms

$$(k, 2k), \quad \text{corresponding to } \lambda = 1,$$

and

$$(k, -k), \quad \text{corresponding to } \lambda = -8.$$

1.13 The matrix of t with respect to the standard basis for $\mathbb{R}^3$ is

$$\mathbf{A} = \begin{pmatrix} 3 & 2 & 2 \\ -2 & -2 & -2 \\ 1 & 2 & 2 \end{pmatrix}.$$

We use Strategy 1.1 to find the eigenvalues and eigenvectors of $\mathbf{A}$, which are the same as those of t.

First we find the eigenvalues of $\mathbf{A}$.

The characteristic equation of $\mathbf{A}$ is

$$\begin{vmatrix} 3 - \lambda & 2 & 2 \\ -2 & -2 - \lambda & -2 \\ 1 & 2 & 2 - \lambda \end{vmatrix} = 0.$$

We expand this determinant and obtain

$$(3 - \lambda) \begin{vmatrix} -2 - \lambda & -2 \\ 2 & 2 - \lambda \end{vmatrix} - 2 \begin{vmatrix} -2 & -2 \\ 1 & 2 - \lambda \end{vmatrix}$$
$$+ 2 \begin{vmatrix} -2 & -2 - \lambda \\ 1 & 2 \end{vmatrix} = 0.$$

Simplifying this expression, we obtain

$$(3 - \lambda)(\lambda^2 - 4 + 4) - 2(2\lambda - 4 + 2) + 2(-4 + 2 + \lambda)$$
$$= (3 - \lambda)\lambda^2 - 2(2\lambda - 2) + 2(\lambda - 2)$$
$$= -\lambda^3 + 3\lambda^2 - 2\lambda$$
$$= -\lambda(\lambda^2 - 3\lambda + 2)$$
$$= -\lambda(\lambda - 2)(\lambda - 1) = 0.$$

The eigenvalues of $\mathbf{A}$ are therefore $\lambda = 2$, $\lambda = 1$ and $\lambda = 0$.

Next we find the eigenvectors of $\mathbf{A}$.

The eigenvector equations are

$$\begin{cases} (3 - \lambda)x + 2y + 2z = 0, \\ -2x + (-2 - \lambda)y - 2z = 0, \\ x + 2y + (2 - \lambda)z = 0. \end{cases}$$

$\boxed{\lambda = 2}$ The eigenvector equations become

$$\begin{cases} x + 2y + 2z = 0, \\ -2x - 4y - 2z = 0, \\ x + 2y = 0. \end{cases}$$

Subtracting the third equation from the first, we obtain $2z = 0$, which implies that $z = 0$. Substituting this into the equations gives the single equation $x + 2y = 0$. Thus the eigenvectors corresponding to $\lambda = 2$ are the non-zero vectors for which $x = -2y$ and $z = 0$; that is, the vectors of the form

$$(-2k, k, 0), \quad \text{where } k \neq 0.$$

$\boxed{\lambda = 1}$ The eigenvector equations become
$$\begin{cases} 2x + 2y + 2z = 0, \\ -2x - 3y - 2z = 0, \\ x + 2y + z = 0. \end{cases}$$
Adding the first and second equations, we obtain $-y = 0$, which implies that $y = 0$. Substituting this into the equations gives the single equation $x + z = 0$. Thus the eigenvectors corresponding to $\lambda = 1$ are the non-zero vectors for which $z = -x$ and $y = 0$; that is, the vectors of the form
$$(k, 0, -k), \quad \text{where } k \neq 0.$$

$\boxed{\lambda = 0}$ The eigenvector equations become
$$\begin{cases} 3x + 2y + 2z = 0, \\ -2x - 2y - 2z = 0, \\ x + 2y + 2z = 0. \end{cases}$$
Adding the first and second equations, we obtain $x = 0$. Substituting this into the equations gives the single equation $y + z = 0$. Thus the eigenvectors corresponding to $\lambda = 0$ are the non-zero vectors for which $x = 0$ and $z = -y$; that is, the vectors of the form
$$(0, k, -k), \quad \text{where } k \neq 0.$$
Thus the eigenvectors of the linear transformation t are the non-zero vectors of the forms
$$(-2k, k, 0), \quad \text{corresponding to } \lambda = 2,$$
$$(k, 0, -k), \quad \text{corresponding to } \lambda = 1,$$
and
$$(0, k, -k), \quad \text{corresponding to } \lambda = 0.$$

1.14 The characteristic equation of $\mathbf{A}$ is
$$\begin{vmatrix} a - \lambda & b \\ c & d - \lambda \end{vmatrix} = 0.$$
We expand this determinant and obtain
$$(a - \lambda)(d - \lambda) - bc = \lambda^2 - (a + d)\lambda + ad - bc = 0.$$
We use the formula for the solution to a quadratic equation to obtain
$$\lambda_1 = \tfrac{1}{2}\left((a + d) + \sqrt{(a + d)^2 - 4(ad - bc)}\right)$$
and
$$\lambda_2 = \tfrac{1}{2}\left((a + d) - \sqrt{(a + d)^2 - 4(ad - bc)}\right).$$
The sum of these eigenvalues is
$$\tfrac{1}{2}(a + d) + \tfrac{1}{2}(a + d) = a + d,$$
as required.

This relationship is true for the eigenvalues of any $n \times n$ matrix, and provides a quick check that sometimes reveals when a mistake has been made in finding the eigenvalues.

1.15 The matrix of t with respect to the standard basis for $\mathbb{R}^3$ is
$$\mathbf{A} = \begin{pmatrix} 0 & 0 & -2 \\ 1 & 2 & 1 \\ 1 & 0 & 3 \end{pmatrix}.$$

We use Strategy 1.1 to find the eigenvalues and eigenvectors of $\mathbf{A}$, which are the same as those of t.

First we find the eigenvalues of $\mathbf{A}$.

The characteristic equation of $\mathbf{A}$ is
$$\begin{vmatrix} -\lambda & 0 & -2 \\ 1 & 2 - \lambda & 1 \\ 1 & 0 & 3 - \lambda \end{vmatrix} = 0.$$
We expand this determinant and obtain
$$-\lambda \begin{vmatrix} 2 - \lambda & 1 \\ 0 & 3 - \lambda \end{vmatrix} - 0 - 2 \begin{vmatrix} 1 & 2 - \lambda \\ 1 & 0 \end{vmatrix} = 0.$$
Simplifying this expression, we obtain
$$-\lambda[(2 - \lambda)(3 - \lambda) - 0] - 2[0 - (2 - \lambda)]$$
$$= (2 - \lambda)[-\lambda(3 - \lambda) + 2]$$
$$= (2 - \lambda)(\lambda^2 - 3\lambda + 2)$$
$$= (2 - \lambda)(\lambda - 2)(\lambda - 1) = 0.$$
The eigenvalues of $\mathbf{A}$ are therefore $\lambda = 2$, $\lambda = 2$ and $\lambda = 1$.

Next we find the eigenvectors of $\mathbf{A}$.

The eigenvector equations are
$$\begin{cases} -\lambda x - 2z = 0, \\ x + (2 - \lambda)y + z = 0, \\ x + (3 - \lambda)z = 0. \end{cases}$$

$\boxed{\lambda = 2}$ The eigenvector equations become
$$\begin{cases} -2x - 2z = 0, \\ x + z = 0, \\ x + z = 0. \end{cases}$$
These equations are equivalent to the single equation $x + z = 0$. There are no constraints on y. Thus the eigenvectors corresponding to $\lambda = 2$ are the non-zero vectors for which $x = -z$; that is, the vectors of the form
$$(-k, l, k), \quad \text{where } k \text{ and } l \text{ are not both } 0.$$
The eigenspace $S(2)$ is the set of vectors
$$\{(-k, l, k) : k, l \in \mathbb{R}\}.$$
Any vector in $S(2)$ can be written as $k(-1, 0, 1) + l(0, 1, 0)$, so
$$\{(-1, 0, 1), (0, 1, 0)\}$$
is a basis for $S(2)$.
Thus $S(2)$ has dimension 2.

$\boxed{\lambda = 1}$ The eigenvector equations become
$$\begin{cases} -x - 2z = 0, \\ x + y + z = 0, \\ x + 2z = 0. \end{cases}$$
The first and third equations imply that $x + 2z = 0$, so $x = -2z$. Substituting this into the second equation, we obtain $y - z = 0$, so $y = z$. Thus the eigenvectors corresponding to $\lambda = 1$ are the non-zero vectors for which $x = -2z$ and $y = z$; that is, the vectors of the form
$$(-2k, k, k), \quad \text{where } k \neq 0.$$

The eigenspace $S(1)$ is the set of vectors
$$\{(-2k, k, k) : k \in \mathbb{R}\}.$$
Any vector in $S(1)$ can be written as $k(-2, 1, 1)$, so
$$\{(-2, 1, 1)\}$$
is a basis for $S(1)$.
Thus $S(1)$ has dimension 1.

2.1 From Exercise 1.5(b) you can see that $(-2, 1)$ and $(1, 2)$ are eigenvectors of t (let $k = 1$). Since $(1, 2)$ is not a multiple of $(-2, 1)$, these two eigenvectors form a basis for $\mathbb{R}^2$.

2.2 Each of the vectors in E is an eigenvector of t:
$$t(0, 1, -1) = (0, 0, 0) = 0(0, 1, -1),$$
$$t(-2, 1, 0) = (4, -2, 0) = -2(-2, 1, 0),$$
$$t(1, 0, -1) = (-3, 0, 3) = -3(1, 0, -1).$$
Thus E is a basis for $\mathbb{R}^3$ consisting of eigenvectors of t; that is, E is an eigenvector basis of t.

2.3 **(a)** The matrix of t with respect to the standard basis for $\mathbb{R}^2$ is
$$\begin{pmatrix} 1 & -2 \\ -2 & -2 \end{pmatrix}.$$
(b) Following Strategy 2.1, first we find the images of the vectors in the basis $E = \{(-2, 1), (1, 2)\}$:
$$t(-2, 1) = (-4, 2), \quad t(1, 2) = (-3, -6).$$
Next we find the E-coordinates of each of these image vectors:
$$t(-2, 1) = 2(-2, 1) + 0(1, 2) = (2, 0)_E,$$
$$t(1, 2) = 0(-2, 1) - 3(1, 2) = (0, -3)_E.$$
So the matrix of t with respect to the eigenvector basis E is
$$\begin{pmatrix} 2 & 0 \\ 0 & -3 \end{pmatrix}.$$

2.4 In Exercise 2.2 you showed that
$$t(0, 1, -1) = 0(0, 1, -1),$$
$$t(-2, 1, 0) = -2(-2, 1, 0),$$
$$t(1, 0, -1) = -3(1, 0, -1).$$
So the eigenvalues of t are 0, -2 and -3, and, by Theorem 2.1, the matrix of t with respect to E is
$$\begin{pmatrix} 0 & 0 & 0 \\ 0 & -2 & 0 \\ 0 & 0 & -3 \end{pmatrix}.$$

2.5 **(a)** $\mathbf{P} = \begin{pmatrix} 1 & 2 \\ 3 & 5 \end{pmatrix}$

(b) $\mathbf{P} = \begin{pmatrix} 0 & -2 & 1 \\ 1 & 1 & 0 \\ -1 & 0 & -1 \end{pmatrix}$

2.6 Let $t : \mathbb{R}^2 \longrightarrow \mathbb{R}^2$ be the linear transformation given by
$$t(x, y) = (x - 2y, -2x - 2y)$$
and let E be the eigenvector basis $\{(-2, 1), (1, 2)\}$ of t. It follows from Exercise 2.3 that $\mathbf{A}$ is the matrix of t with respect to the standard basis for $\mathbb{R}^2$ and $\mathbf{D}$ is the matrix of t with respect to the eigenvector basis E. By Theorem 2.3, $\mathbf{D} = \mathbf{P}^{-1}\mathbf{A}\mathbf{P}$, where $\mathbf{P}$ is the transition matrix from E to the standard basis for $\mathbb{R}^2$; that is,
$$\mathbf{P} = \begin{pmatrix} -2 & 1 \\ 1 & 2 \end{pmatrix}.$$

2.7 **(a)** $\mathbf{D}^5 = \begin{pmatrix} 2^5 & 0 \\ 0 & (-3)^5 \end{pmatrix} = \begin{pmatrix} 32 & 0 \\ 0 & -243 \end{pmatrix}$

(b) It follows from Exercise 2.6 that $\mathbf{A}^5 = \mathbf{P}\mathbf{D}^5\mathbf{P}^{-1}$, where $\mathbf{D}$ is as in part (a) and
$$\mathbf{P} = \begin{pmatrix} -2 & 1 \\ 1 & 2 \end{pmatrix}.$$
Since $\mathbf{P}^{-1} = -\frac{1}{5}\begin{pmatrix} 2 & -1 \\ -1 & -2 \end{pmatrix}$, it follows that
$$\mathbf{A}^5 = \begin{pmatrix} -2 & 1 \\ 1 & 2 \end{pmatrix}\begin{pmatrix} 32 & 0 \\ 0 & -243 \end{pmatrix}\tfrac{1}{5}\begin{pmatrix} -2 & 1 \\ 1 & 2 \end{pmatrix}$$
$$= \begin{pmatrix} -23 & -110 \\ -110 & -188 \end{pmatrix}.$$

2.8 We use Strategy 2.1.

You found the eigenvalues and eigenvectors of $\mathbf{A}$ in Exercise 1.6.

The eigenvalues of $\mathbf{A}$ are $\lambda = 6$, $\lambda = 3$ and $\lambda = 0$.

The eigenvectors of $\mathbf{A}$ are the non-zero vectors of the forms
$$(2k, 2k, k), \text{ corresponding to } \lambda = 6,$$
$$(-2k, k, 2k), \text{ corresponding to } \lambda = 3,$$
and
$$(k, -2k, 2k), \text{ corresponding to } \lambda = 0.$$
It follows from Theorem 2.4 that we can form an eigenvector basis of $\mathbf{A}$ by taking one eigenvector corresponding to each of the three distinct eigenvalues. For example,
$$E = \{(2, 2, 1), (-2, 1, 2), (1, -2, 2)\}$$
is an eigenvector basis of $\mathbf{A}$.

We use the eigenvectors in E to form the columns of the transition matrix:
$$\mathbf{P} = \begin{pmatrix} 2 & -2 & 1 \\ 2 & 1 & -2 \\ 1 & 2 & 2 \end{pmatrix}.$$
We use the eigenvalues corresponding to the eigenvectors in E to form the diagonal matrix:
$$\mathbf{P}^{-1}\mathbf{A}\mathbf{P} = \mathbf{D} = \begin{pmatrix} 6 & 0 & 0 \\ 0 & 3 & 0 \\ 0 & 0 & 0 \end{pmatrix}.$$

2.9 The characteristic equation of $\mathbf{A}$ is

$$\begin{vmatrix} 1-\lambda & 0 & 0 \\ 0 & 2-\lambda & 1 \\ 0 & 1 & 2-\lambda \end{vmatrix} = 0.$$

We expand this determinant and obtain

$$(1-\lambda)((2-\lambda)^2 - 1) = 0,$$

which simplifies to

$$(1-\lambda)(\lambda^2 - 4\lambda + 3) = (1-\lambda)(\lambda-1)(\lambda-3) = 0.$$

The eigenvalues of $\mathbf{A}$ are therefore $\lambda = 3$, $\lambda = 1$ and $\lambda = 1$.

To find the eigenspaces of $\mathbf{A}$, we consider the eigenvector equations

$$\begin{cases} (1-\lambda)x & = 0, \\ (2-\lambda)y + & z = 0, \\ y + (2-\lambda)z = 0, \end{cases}$$

for each of the eigenvalues.

$\boxed{\lambda = 3}$ The eigenvector equations become

$$\begin{cases} -2x & = 0, \\ -y + z = 0, \\ y - z = 0. \end{cases}$$

So $x = 0$, $y = z$ and $S(3) = \{(0, k, k) : k \in \mathbb{R}\}$.

$\boxed{\lambda = 1}$ The eigenvector equations become

$$\begin{cases} 0x & = 0, \\ y + z = 0, \\ y + z = 0. \end{cases}$$

So $z = -y$ and $S(1) = \{(k, l, -l) : k, l \in \mathbb{R}\}$.

A basis for $S(3)$ is $\{(0, 1, 1)\}$ and a basis for $S(1)$ is $\{(1, 0, 0), (0, 1, -1)\}$. The set

$$E = \{(0, 1, 1), (1, 0, 0), (0, 1, -1)\}$$

contains three vectors, so it is an eigenvector basis of $\mathbf{A}$.

We use the eigenvectors in E to form the columns of the transition matrix:

$$\mathbf{P} = \begin{pmatrix} 0 & 1 & 0 \\ 1 & 0 & 1 \\ 1 & 0 & -1 \end{pmatrix}.$$

We use the eigenvalues corresponding to the eigenvectors in E to form the diagonal matrix:

$$\mathbf{P}^{-1}\mathbf{A}\mathbf{P} = \mathbf{D} = \begin{pmatrix} 3 & 0 & 0 \\ 0 & 1 & 0 \\ 0 & 0 & 1 \end{pmatrix}.$$

There are many possible solutions to each of the remaining exercises in this section, representing different orderings of the eigenvectors.

2.10 (a) The matrix of t with respect to the standard basis for $\mathbb{R}^2$ is

$$\mathbf{A} = \begin{pmatrix} 1 & 1 \\ 1 & 1 \end{pmatrix}.$$

(b) First we find the eigenvalues of $\mathbf{A}$. The characteristic equation of $\mathbf{A}$ is

$$\begin{vmatrix} 1-\lambda & 1 \\ 1 & 1-\lambda \end{vmatrix} = 0.$$

We expand this determinant and obtain

$$(1-\lambda)^2 - 1 = 0,$$

which simplifies to

$$\lambda^2 - 2\lambda = \lambda(\lambda - 2) = 0.$$

The eigenvalues of $\mathbf{A}$ are therefore $\lambda = 2$ and $\lambda = 0$.

Next we find the eigenvectors of $\mathbf{A}$. The eigenvector equations are

$$\begin{cases} (1-\lambda)x + & y = 0, \\ x + (1-\lambda)y = 0. \end{cases}$$

$\boxed{\lambda = 2}$ The eigenvector equations become

$$\begin{cases} -x + y = 0, \\ x - y = 0. \end{cases}$$

These equations give $x = y$. Thus the eigenvectors corresponding to $\lambda = 2$ are the vectors of the form

$$(k, k), \quad \text{where } k \neq 0.$$

$\boxed{\lambda = 0}$ The eigenvector equations become

$$\begin{cases} x + y = 0, \\ x + y = 0. \end{cases}$$

These equations give $x = -y$. Thus the eigenvectors corresponding to $\lambda = 0$ are the vectors of the form

$$(k, -k), \quad \text{where } k \neq 0.$$

The eigenvectors of $\mathbf{A}$ are the eigenvectors of t. So, for example, $\{(1, 1), (1, -1)\}$ is an eigenvector basis of t since $(1, -1)$ is not a multiple of $(1, 1)$.

(c) It follows from Theorem 2.1 that

$$\mathbf{D} = \begin{pmatrix} 2 & 0 \\ 0 & 0 \end{pmatrix}.$$

(d) It follows from Theorem 2.3 that $\mathbf{P}$ is the transition matrix from E to the standard basis for $\mathbb{R}^2$. So

$$\mathbf{P} = \begin{pmatrix} 1 & 1 \\ 1 & -1 \end{pmatrix}.$$

2.11 We use Strategy 2.2.

The eigenvalues of $\mathbf{A}$ are $\lambda = 1$ and $\lambda = -8$.

The eigenvectors of $\mathbf{A}$ are the non-zero vectors of the forms

$$(k, 2k), \quad \text{corresponding to } \lambda = 1,$$

and

$$(k, -k), \quad \text{corresponding to } \lambda = -8.$$

It follows from Theorem 2.4 that we can form an eigenvector basis of $\mathbf{A}$ by taking one eigenvector corresponding to each eigenvalue. For example,

$$E = \{(1, 2), (1, -1)\}$$

is an eigenvector basis of $\mathbf{A}$.

We use the eigenvectors in E to form the columns of the transition matrix:

$$\mathbf{P} = \begin{pmatrix} 1 & 1 \\ 2 & -1 \end{pmatrix}.$$

We use the eigenvalues to form the diagonal matrix:

$$\mathbf{P}^{-1}\mathbf{A}\mathbf{P} = \mathbf{D} = \begin{pmatrix} 1 & 0 \\ 0 & -8 \end{pmatrix}.$$

2.12 We use Strategy 2.2.

The eigenvalues of $\mathbf{A}$ are $\lambda = 2$, $\lambda = 1$ and $\lambda = 0$.

The eigenvectors of $\mathbf{A}$ are the non-zero vectors of the forms

$(-2k, k, 0)$, corresponding to $\lambda = 2$,

$(k, 0, -k)$, corresponding to $\lambda = 1$,

and

$(0, k, -k)$, corresponding to $\lambda = 0$.

It follows from Theorem 2.4 that we can form an eigenvector basis of $\mathbf{A}$ by taking one eigenvector corresponding to each of the three distinct eigenvalues. For example,

$$E = \{(-2, 1, 0), (1, 0, -1), (0, 1, -1)\}$$

is an eigenvector basis of $\mathbf{A}$.

We use the eigenvectors in E to form the columns of the transition matrix:

$$\mathbf{P} = \begin{pmatrix} -2 & 1 & 0 \\ 1 & 0 & 1 \\ 0 & -1 & -1 \end{pmatrix}.$$

We use the eigenvalues to form the diagonal matrix:

$$\mathbf{P}^{-1}\mathbf{A}\mathbf{P} = \mathbf{D} = \begin{pmatrix} 2 & 0 & 0 \\ 0 & 1 & 0 \\ 0 & 0 & 0 \end{pmatrix}.$$

2.13 The eigenvalues of $\mathbf{A}$ are $\lambda = 2$, $\lambda = 2$ and $\lambda = 1$.

The eigenspaces of $\mathbf{A}$ are $S(2) = \{(-k, l, k) : k, l \in \mathbb{R}\}$ and $S(1) = \{(-2k, k, k) : k \in \mathbb{R}\}$. A basis for $S(2)$ is $\{(-1, 0, 1), (0, 1, 0)\}$ and a basis for $S(1)$ is $\{(-2, 1, 1)\}$. The set

$$E = \{(-1, 0, 1), (0, 1, 0), (-2, 1, 1)\}$$

contains three vectors, so it is an eigenvector basis of $\mathbf{A}$.

We use the eigenvectors in E to form the columns of the transition matrix:

$$\mathbf{P} = \begin{pmatrix} -1 & 0 & -2 \\ 0 & 1 & 1 \\ 1 & 0 & 1 \end{pmatrix}.$$

We use the eigenvalues to form the diagonal matrix:

$$\mathbf{P}^{-1}\mathbf{A}\mathbf{P} = \mathbf{D} = \begin{pmatrix} 2 & 0 & 0 \\ 0 & 2 & 0 \\ 0 & 0 & 1 \end{pmatrix}.$$

3.1 (a) We have

$(2k, 2k, k) \cdot (-2l, l, 2l) = -4kl + 2kl + 2kl = 0,$

$(2k, 2k, k) \cdot (m, -2m, 2m) = 2km - 4km + 2km = 0,$

$(-2l, l, 2l) \cdot (m, -2m, 2m) = -2lm - 2lm + 4lm = 0.$

Thus the given vectors form an orthogonal set. Since there are three of them, they form an orthogonal basis for $\mathbb{R}^3$.

(b) $\|\mathbf{v}_1\| = \|(2k, 2k, k)\| = \sqrt{4k^2 + 4k^2 + k^2}$
$$= \sqrt{9k^2} = 3k,$$

$\|\mathbf{v}_2\| = \|(-2l, l, 2l)\| = \sqrt{4l^2 + l^2 + 4l^2}$
$$= \sqrt{9l^2} = 3l,$$

$\|\mathbf{v}_3\| = \|(m, -2m, 2m)\| = \sqrt{m^2 + 4m^2 + 4m^2}$
$$= \sqrt{9m^2} = 3m.$$

Thus $\|\mathbf{v}_1\| = \|\mathbf{v}_2\| = \|\mathbf{v}_3\| = 1$ if

$$k = l = m = \tfrac{1}{3}.$$

3.2 $\mathbf{P}^T\mathbf{P} = \begin{pmatrix} \frac{2}{3} & \frac{2}{3} & \frac{1}{3} \\ -\frac{2}{3} & \frac{1}{3} & \frac{2}{3} \\ \frac{1}{3} & -\frac{2}{3} & \frac{2}{3} \end{pmatrix} \begin{pmatrix} \frac{2}{3} & -\frac{2}{3} & \frac{1}{3} \\ \frac{2}{3} & \frac{1}{3} & -\frac{2}{3} \\ \frac{1}{3} & \frac{2}{3} & \frac{2}{3} \end{pmatrix}$

$$= \begin{pmatrix} \frac{9}{9} & 0 & 0 \\ 0 & \frac{9}{9} & 0 \\ 0 & 0 & \frac{9}{9} \end{pmatrix} = \begin{pmatrix} 1 & 0 & 0 \\ 0 & 1 & 0 \\ 0 & 0 & 1 \end{pmatrix} = \mathbf{I}$$

By Unit LA2, Theorem 5.5, $\mathbf{P}^T\mathbf{P} = \mathbf{I}$ implies that $\mathbf{P}^T = \mathbf{P}^{-1}$.

3.3 (a) We use Strategy 3.1.

The characteristic equation of $\mathbf{A}$ is

$$\begin{vmatrix} 9 - \lambda & -2 \\ -2 & 6 - \lambda \end{vmatrix} = 0.$$

We expand this determinant and obtain

$$(9 - \lambda)(6 - \lambda) - 4 = 0,$$

which simplifies to

$$\lambda^2 - 15\lambda + 50 = (\lambda - 10)(\lambda - 5) = 0.$$

The eigenvalues of $\mathbf{A}$ are therefore $\lambda = 10$ and $\lambda = 5$.

Next we find orthonormal bases for the eigenspaces. The eigenvector equations are

$$\begin{cases} (9 - \lambda)x - & 2y = 0, \\ -2x + & (6 - \lambda)y = 0. \end{cases}$$

$\boxed{\lambda = 10}$ The eigenvector equations become

$$\begin{cases} -x - 2y = 0, \\ -2x - 4y = 0. \end{cases}$$

These equations are equivalent to the single equation

$$x + 2y = 0,$$

that is, $x = -2y$. Thus the eigenvectors corresponding to $\lambda = 10$ are the non-zero vectors of the form $(2k, -k)$.

An eigenvector of unit length corresponding to $\lambda = 10$ is $\left(\frac{2}{\sqrt{5}}, -\frac{1}{\sqrt{5}}\right)$.

$\boxed{\lambda = 5}$ The eigenvector equations become
$$\begin{cases} 4x - 2y = 0, \\ -2x + y = 0. \end{cases}$$
These equations are equivalent to the single equation
$$2x - y = 0,$$
that is, $y = 2x$. Thus the eigenvectors corresponding to $\lambda = 5$ are the non-zero vectors of the form $(k, 2k)$.

An eigenvector of unit length corresponding to $\lambda = 5$ is $\left(\frac{1}{\sqrt{5}}, \frac{2}{\sqrt{5}}\right)$.

It follows from Theorem 3.1 that an orthonormal eigenvector basis of $\mathbf{A}$ is
$$E = \left\{ \left(\frac{2}{\sqrt{5}}, -\frac{1}{\sqrt{5}}\right), \left(\frac{1}{\sqrt{5}}, \frac{2}{\sqrt{5}}\right) \right\}.$$
We use the eigenvectors in E to form the columns of the transition matrix:
$$\mathbf{P} = \begin{pmatrix} \frac{2}{\sqrt{5}} & \frac{1}{\sqrt{5}} \\ -\frac{1}{\sqrt{5}} & \frac{2}{\sqrt{5}} \end{pmatrix}.$$
We use the eigenvalues corresponding to the eigenvectors in E to form the diagonal matrix:
$$\mathbf{P}^T \mathbf{A} \mathbf{P} = \mathbf{D} = \begin{pmatrix} 10 & 0 \\ 0 & 5 \end{pmatrix}.$$

(b) The eigenvalues of $\mathbf{A}$ are given as $\lambda = 6$, $\lambda = 3$ and $\lambda = 2$.

Now we find an orthonormal eigenvector basis of $\mathbf{A}$.

The eigenvector equations are
$$\begin{cases} (5 - \lambda)x - y - z = 0, \\ -x + (3 - \lambda)y + z = 0, \\ -x + y + (3 - \lambda)z = 0. \end{cases}$$

$\boxed{\lambda = 6}$ The eigenvector equations become
$$\begin{cases} -x - y - z = 0, \\ -x - 3y + z = 0, \\ -x + y - 3z = 0. \end{cases}$$
Adding the first and second equations together, we obtain
$$-2x - 4y = 0,$$
so $x = -2y$. Substituting this into the third equation, we obtain
$$3y - 3z = 0,$$
so $z = y$. Thus the eigenvectors corresponding to $\lambda = 6$ are the non-zero vectors of the form $(-2k, k, k)$.

An eigenvector of unit length corresponding to $\lambda = 6$ is $\left(-\frac{2}{\sqrt{6}}, \frac{1}{\sqrt{6}}, \frac{1}{\sqrt{6}}\right)$.

$\boxed{\lambda = 3}$ The eigenvector equations become
$$\begin{cases} 2x - y - z = 0, \\ -x + z = 0, \\ -x + y = 0. \end{cases}$$
The second and third equations imply that $z = x$ and that $y = x$. These satisfy the first equation. Thus the eigenvectors corresponding to $\lambda = 3$ are the non-zero vectors of the form (k, k, k).

An eigenvalue of unit length corresponding to $\lambda = 3$ is $\left(\frac{1}{\sqrt{3}}, \frac{1}{\sqrt{3}}, \frac{1}{\sqrt{3}}\right)$.

$\boxed{\lambda = 2}$ The eigenvector equations become
$$\begin{cases} 3x - y - z = 0, \\ -x + y + z = 0, \\ -x + y + z = 0. \end{cases}$$
Adding the first and second equations together, we obtain
$$2x = 0,$$
which implies that $x = 0$. Substituting this into the third equation, we obtain
$$y + z = 0,$$
which implies that $z = -y$. Thus the eigenvectors corresponding to $\lambda = 2$ are the non-zero vectors of the form $(0, k, -k)$.

An eigenvector of unit length corresponding to $\lambda = 2$ is $\left(0, \frac{1}{\sqrt{2}}, -\frac{1}{\sqrt{2}}\right)$.

It follows from Theorem 3.1 that an orthonormal eigenvector basis of $\mathbf{A}$ is
$$E = \left\{ \left(-\frac{2}{\sqrt{6}}, \frac{1}{\sqrt{6}}, \frac{1}{\sqrt{6}}\right), \left(\frac{1}{\sqrt{3}}, \frac{1}{\sqrt{3}}, \frac{1}{\sqrt{3}}\right), \right.$$
$$\left. \left(0, \frac{1}{\sqrt{2}}, -\frac{1}{\sqrt{2}}\right) \right\}.$$
We use the eigenvectors in E to form the columns of the transition matrix:
$$\mathbf{P} = \begin{pmatrix} -\frac{2}{\sqrt{6}} & \frac{1}{\sqrt{3}} & 0 \\ \frac{1}{\sqrt{6}} & \frac{1}{\sqrt{3}} & \frac{1}{\sqrt{2}} \\ \frac{1}{\sqrt{6}} & \frac{1}{\sqrt{3}} & -\frac{1}{\sqrt{2}} \end{pmatrix}.$$
We use the eigenvalues corresponding to the eigenvectors in E to form the diagonal matrix:
$$\mathbf{P}^T \mathbf{A} \mathbf{P} = \mathbf{D} = \begin{pmatrix} 6 & 0 & 0 \\ 0 & 3 & 0 \\ 0 & 0 & 2 \end{pmatrix}.$$

3.4 We use Strategy 3.1.

The eigenvalues of $\mathbf{A}$ are $\lambda = 3$, $\lambda = 1$ and $\lambda = 1$.

The eigenvectors of $\mathbf{A}$ are the non-zero vectors of the forms
$$(0, k, k), \text{ corresponding to } \lambda = 3,$$
and
$$(k, l, -l), \text{ corresponding to } \lambda = 1.$$
Now, $(0, k, k) = k(0, 1, 1)$, so a basis for $S(3)$ is $\{(0, 1, 1)\}$.

An orthonormal basis for $S(3)$ is
$$\left\{ \left(0, \frac{1}{\sqrt{2}}, \frac{1}{\sqrt{2}}\right) \right\}.$$
Also, $(k, l, -l) = k(1, 0, 0) + l(0, 1, -1)$, so a basis for $S(1)$ is $\{(1, 0, 0), (0, 1, -1)\}$.

Notice that $(1, 0, 0) \cdot (0, 1, -1) = 0$, so these basis vectors are orthogonal. An orthonormal basis for $S(1)$ is therefore
$$\left\{ (1, 0, 0), \left(0, \frac{1}{\sqrt{2}}, -\frac{1}{\sqrt{2}}\right) \right\}.$$

An orthonormal eigenvector basis of $\mathbf{A}$ is therefore
$$E = \left\{ \left(0, \tfrac{1}{\sqrt{2}}, \tfrac{1}{\sqrt{2}}\right), (1,0,0), \left(0, \tfrac{1}{\sqrt{2}}, -\tfrac{1}{\sqrt{2}}\right) \right\}.$$
We use the eigenvectors in E to form the columns of the transition matrix:
$$\mathbf{P} = \begin{pmatrix} 0 & 1 & 0 \\ \tfrac{1}{\sqrt{2}} & 0 & \tfrac{1}{\sqrt{2}} \\ \tfrac{1}{\sqrt{2}} & 0 & -\tfrac{1}{\sqrt{2}} \end{pmatrix}.$$
We use the eigenvalues corresponding to the eigenvectors in E to form the diagonal matrix:
$$\mathbf{P}^T \mathbf{A P} = \mathbf{D} = \begin{pmatrix} 3 & 0 & 0 \\ 0 & 1 & 0 \\ 0 & 0 & 1 \end{pmatrix}.$$

3.5 By Theorem 3.2, to prove that the product $\mathbf{PQ}$ is orthogonal, it is sufficient to show that $(\mathbf{PQ})^T = (\mathbf{PQ})^{-1}$.
But
$$(\mathbf{PQ})^T = \mathbf{Q}^T \mathbf{P}^T = \mathbf{Q}^{-1} \mathbf{P}^{-1} = (\mathbf{PQ})^{-1}.$$

3.6 (a) To verify that $\mathbf{A}$ is orthogonal, it is sufficient to show that $\mathbf{A}^T \mathbf{A} = \mathbf{I}$.
$$\mathbf{A}^T \mathbf{A} = \begin{pmatrix} 0 & 0 & 1 \\ 0 & 1 & 0 \\ -1 & 0 & 0 \end{pmatrix} \begin{pmatrix} 0 & 0 & -1 \\ 0 & 1 & 0 \\ 1 & 0 & 0 \end{pmatrix}$$
$$= \begin{pmatrix} 1 & 0 & 0 \\ 0 & 1 & 0 \\ 0 & 0 & 1 \end{pmatrix} = \mathbf{I},$$
so $\mathbf{A}$ is orthogonal.

(Alternatively, we could have shown that the vectors $(0,0,1)$, $(0,1,0)$ and $(-1,0,0)$ form an orthonormal basis for $\mathbb{R}^3$.)

(b) We evaluate the determinant of $\mathbf{A}$:
$$\begin{vmatrix} 0 & 0 & -1 \\ 0 & 1 & 0 \\ 1 & 0 & 0 \end{vmatrix} = 0 - 0 - \begin{vmatrix} 0 & 1 \\ 1 & 0 \end{vmatrix} = 1.$$
Therefore $\mathbf{A}$ represents a rotation of $\mathbb{R}^3$.

There are many possible solutions to each of the remaining exercises in this section, representing different orderings of the eigenvectors.

3.7 We use Strategy 3.1.
The characteristic equation of $\mathbf{A}$ is
$$\begin{vmatrix} 5 - \lambda & -1 \\ -1 & 5 - \lambda \end{vmatrix} = 0.$$
We expand this determinant and obtain
$$(5 - \lambda)^2 - 1 = 0,$$
which simplifies to
$$\lambda^2 - 10\lambda + 24 = (\lambda - 6)(\lambda - 4) = 0.$$
The eigenvalues of $\mathbf{A}$ are therefore $\lambda = 6$ and $\lambda = 4$.
The eigenvector equations are
$$\begin{cases} (5 - \lambda)x - \quad\;\; y = 0, \\ -x + (5 - \lambda)y = 0. \end{cases}$$

$\boxed{\lambda = 6}$ The eigenvector equations become
$$\begin{cases} -x - y = 0, \\ -x - y = 0. \end{cases}$$
These equations are equivalent to the single equation $x + y = 0$; that is, $y = -x$. Thus the eigenvectors corresponding to $\lambda = 6$ are the non-zero vectors of the form $(k, -k)$.
An eigenvector of unit length corresponding to $\lambda = 6$ is $\left(\tfrac{1}{\sqrt{2}}, -\tfrac{1}{\sqrt{2}}\right)$.

$\boxed{\lambda = 4}$ The eigenvector equations become
$$\begin{cases} x - y = 0, \\ -x + y = 0. \end{cases}$$
These equations are equivalent to the single equation $x - y = 0$; that is, $y = x$. Thus the eigenvectors corresponding to $\lambda = 4$ are the non-zero vectors of the form (k, k).
An eigenvector of unit length corresponding to $\lambda = 4$ is $\left(\tfrac{1}{\sqrt{2}}, \tfrac{1}{\sqrt{2}}\right)$.

An orthonormal eigenvector basis of $\mathbf{A}$ is therefore
$$E = \left\{ \left(\tfrac{1}{\sqrt{2}}, -\tfrac{1}{\sqrt{2}}\right), \left(\tfrac{1}{\sqrt{2}}, \tfrac{1}{\sqrt{2}}\right) \right\}.$$
We use the eigenvectors in E to form the columns of the transition matrix:
$$\mathbf{P} = \begin{pmatrix} \tfrac{1}{\sqrt{2}} & \tfrac{1}{\sqrt{2}} \\ -\tfrac{1}{\sqrt{2}} & \tfrac{1}{\sqrt{2}} \end{pmatrix}.$$
We use the eigenvalues to form the diagonal matrix:
$$\mathbf{P}^T \mathbf{A P} = \mathbf{D} = \begin{pmatrix} 6 & 0 \\ 0 & 4 \end{pmatrix}.$$

3.8 We use Strategy 3.1.
The characteristic equation of $\mathbf{A}$ is
$$\begin{vmatrix} -\lambda & 1 & 0 \\ 1 & -\lambda & 0 \\ 0 & 0 & -\lambda \end{vmatrix} = 0.$$
We expand this determinant and obtain
$$-\lambda \begin{vmatrix} -\lambda & 0 \\ 0 & -\lambda \end{vmatrix} - \begin{vmatrix} 1 & 0 \\ 0 & -\lambda \end{vmatrix} + 0 = 0,$$
which simplifies to
$$-\lambda(-\lambda)^2 - (-\lambda) = -\lambda(\lambda^2 - 1)$$
$$= -\lambda(\lambda - 1)(\lambda + 1) = 0.$$
The eigenvalues of $\mathbf{A}$ are therefore $\lambda = 1$, $\lambda = 0$ and $\lambda = -1$.
The eigenvector equations are
$$\begin{cases} -\lambda x + \quad y \quad\;\; = 0, \\ x - \lambda y \quad\;\; = 0, \\ \quad\quad\quad - \lambda z = 0. \end{cases}$$

$\boxed{\lambda = 1}$ The eigenvector equations become
$$\begin{cases} -x + y \quad\;\; = 0, \\ x - y \quad\;\; = 0, \\ \quad\quad\; - z = 0. \end{cases}$$

The third equation implies that $z = 0$. The first and second equations imply that $y = x$. Thus the eigenvectors corresponding to $\lambda = 1$ are the non-zero vectors of the form $(k, k, 0)$.

An eigenvector of unit length corresponding to $\lambda = 1$ is $\left(\frac{1}{\sqrt{2}}, \frac{1}{\sqrt{2}}, 0\right)$.

$\boxed{\lambda = 0}$ The eigenvector equations become
$$\begin{cases} y & = 0, \\ x & = 0, \\ & 0z = 0. \end{cases}$$
The first two equations imply that $y = x = 0$. The third equation gives no constraints on z. Thus the eigenvectors corresponding to $\lambda = 0$ are the non-zero vectors of the form $(0, 0, k)$.

An eigenvector of unit length corresponding to $\lambda = 0$ is $(0, 0, 1)$.

$\boxed{\lambda = -1}$ The eigenvector equations become
$$\begin{cases} x + y & = 0, \\ x + y & = 0, \\ & z = 0. \end{cases}$$
The first two equations imply that $y = -x$. The third equation gives $z = 0$. Thus the eigenvectors corresponding to $\lambda = -1$ are the non-zero vectors of the form $(k, -k, 0)$.

An eigenvector of unit length corresponding to $\lambda = -1$ is $\left(\frac{1}{\sqrt{2}}, -\frac{1}{\sqrt{2}}, 0\right)$.

An orthonormal eigenvector basis of $\mathbf{A}$ is therefore
$$E = \left\{ \left(\tfrac{1}{\sqrt{2}}, \tfrac{1}{\sqrt{2}}, 0\right), (0, 0, 1), \left(\tfrac{1}{\sqrt{2}}, -\tfrac{1}{\sqrt{2}}, 0\right) \right\}.$$
We use the eigenvectors in E to form the columns of the transition matrix:
$$\mathbf{P} = \begin{pmatrix} \frac{1}{\sqrt{2}} & 0 & \frac{1}{\sqrt{2}} \\ \frac{1}{\sqrt{2}} & 0 & -\frac{1}{\sqrt{2}} \\ 0 & 1 & 0 \end{pmatrix}.$$
We use the eigenvalues to form the diagonal matrix:
$$\mathbf{P}^T \mathbf{A} \mathbf{P} = \mathbf{D} = \begin{pmatrix} 1 & 0 & 0 \\ 0 & 0 & 0 \\ 0 & 0 & -1 \end{pmatrix}.$$

3.9 We use Strategies 3.1 and 3.2.

The characteristic equation of $\mathbf{A}$ is
$$\begin{vmatrix} 1 - \lambda & -4 & 2 \\ -4 & 1 - \lambda & -2 \\ 2 & -2 & -2 - \lambda \end{vmatrix} = 0.$$
We expand this determinant and obtain
$$(1 - \lambda) \begin{vmatrix} 1 - \lambda & -2 \\ -2 & -2 - \lambda \end{vmatrix} + 4 \begin{vmatrix} -4 & -2 \\ 2 & -2 - \lambda \end{vmatrix}$$
$$+ 2 \begin{vmatrix} -4 & 1 - \lambda \\ 2 & -2 \end{vmatrix} = 0,$$

which simplifies to
$$(1 - \lambda)[(1 - \lambda)(-2 - \lambda) - 4] + 4[-4(-2 - \lambda) + 4]$$
$$+ 2[8 - 2(1 - \lambda)]$$
$$= (1 - \lambda)\left(\lambda^2 + \lambda - 6\right) + 4(4\lambda + 12) + 2(2\lambda + 6)$$
$$= (1 - \lambda)(\lambda + 3)(\lambda - 2) + 16(\lambda + 3) + 4(\lambda + 3)$$
$$= (\lambda + 3)(-\lambda^2 + 3\lambda + 18)$$
$$= -(\lambda + 3)(\lambda - 6)(\lambda + 3) = 0.$$
The eigenvalues of $\mathbf{A}$ are therefore $\lambda = 6$, $\lambda = -3$ and $\lambda = -3$.

Next we find orthonormal bases for the eigenspaces.

The eigenvector equations are
$$\begin{cases} (1 - \lambda)x - & 4y + & 2z = 0, \\ -4x + (1 - \lambda)y - & & 2z = 0, \\ 2x - & 2y + (-2 - \lambda)z = 0. \end{cases}$$

$\boxed{\lambda = 6}$ The eigenvector equations become
$$\begin{cases} -5x - 4y + 2z = 0, \\ -4x - 5y - 2z = 0, \\ 2x - 2y - 8z = 0. \end{cases}$$
Adding the first and second equations gives $-9x - 9y = 0$, which implies that $y = -x$. Substituting this in the third equation gives $4x - 8z = 0$, which implies that $x = 2z$. Thus the eigenvectors corresponding to $\lambda = 6$ are the non-zero vectors of the form $(2k, -2k, k)$.

Now, $(2k, -2k, k) = k(2, -2, 1)$, so $\{(2, -2, 1)\}$ is a basis for $S(6)$.

An orthonormal basis for $S(6)$ is
$$\left\{ \left(\tfrac{2}{3}, -\tfrac{2}{3}, \tfrac{1}{3}\right) \right\}.$$

$\boxed{\lambda = -3}$ The eigenvector equations become
$$\begin{cases} 4x - 4y + 2z = 0, \\ -4x + 4y - 2z = 0, \\ 2x - 2y + z = 0. \end{cases}$$
These equations are all equivalent to the single equation
$$2x - 2y + z = 0,$$
so $z = 2y - 2x$. Thus the eigenvectors corresponding to $\lambda = -3$ are the non-zero vectors of the form $(k, l, 2(l - k))$.

Now, $(k, l, 2(l - k)) = k(1, 0, -2) + l(0, 1, 2)$, so
$$\{(1, 0, -2), (0, 1, 2)\}$$
is a basis for $S(-3)$.

To find an orthogonal basis for $S(-3)$, we use the Gram–Schmidt orthogonalisation process.

Let the basis we seek be $\{\mathbf{v}_1, \mathbf{v}_2\}$.

Let $\mathbf{v}_1 = (1, 0, -2)$.

Then let
$$\mathbf{v}_2 = (0, 1, 2) - \left(\frac{(1, 0, -2) \cdot (0, 1, 2)}{(1, 0, -2) \cdot (1, 0, -2)} \right) (1, 0, -2)$$
$$= (0, 1, 2) + \tfrac{4}{5}(1, 0, -2) = \left(\tfrac{4}{5}, 1, \tfrac{2}{5}\right).$$

An orthonormal basis for $S(-3)$ is therefore

$$\left\{ \left(\tfrac{1}{\sqrt{5}}, 0, -\tfrac{2}{\sqrt{5}} \right), \left(\tfrac{4}{\sqrt{45}}, \tfrac{5}{\sqrt{45}}, \tfrac{2}{\sqrt{45}} \right) \right\}.$$

An orthonormal eigenvector basis of $\mathbf{A}$ is therefore

$$\left\{ \left(\tfrac{2}{3}, -\tfrac{2}{3}, \tfrac{1}{3} \right), \left(\tfrac{1}{\sqrt{5}}, 0, -\tfrac{2}{\sqrt{5}} \right), \left(\tfrac{4}{\sqrt{45}}, \tfrac{5}{\sqrt{45}}, \tfrac{2}{\sqrt{45}} \right) \right\}.$$

We use the eigenvectors in this basis to form the columns of the transition matrix:

$$\mathbf{P} = \begin{pmatrix} \tfrac{2}{3} & \tfrac{1}{\sqrt{5}} & \tfrac{4}{\sqrt{45}} \\ -\tfrac{2}{3} & 0 & \tfrac{5}{\sqrt{45}} \\ \tfrac{1}{3} & -\tfrac{2}{\sqrt{5}} & \tfrac{2}{\sqrt{45}} \end{pmatrix}.$$

We use the eigenvalues to form the diagonal matrix:

$$\mathbf{P}^T \mathbf{A} \mathbf{P} = \mathbf{D} = \begin{pmatrix} 6 & 0 & 0 \\ 0 & -3 & 0 \\ 0 & 0 & -3 \end{pmatrix}.$$

3.10 (a) To verify that $\mathbf{A}$ is orthogonal, it is sufficient to show that $\mathbf{A}^T \mathbf{A} = \mathbf{I}$.

$$\mathbf{A}^T \mathbf{A} = \begin{pmatrix} \tfrac{2}{7} & -\tfrac{6}{7} & \tfrac{3}{7} \\ \tfrac{6}{7} & \tfrac{3}{7} & \tfrac{2}{7} \\ -\tfrac{3}{7} & \tfrac{2}{7} & \tfrac{6}{7} \end{pmatrix} \begin{pmatrix} \tfrac{2}{7} & \tfrac{6}{7} & -\tfrac{3}{7} \\ -\tfrac{6}{7} & \tfrac{3}{7} & \tfrac{2}{7} \\ \tfrac{3}{7} & \tfrac{2}{7} & \tfrac{6}{7} \end{pmatrix}$$

$$= \begin{pmatrix} \tfrac{49}{49} & 0 & 0 \\ 0 & \tfrac{49}{49} & 0 \\ 0 & 0 & \tfrac{49}{49} \end{pmatrix} = \begin{pmatrix} 1 & 0 & 0 \\ 0 & 1 & 0 \\ 0 & 0 & 1 \end{pmatrix} = \mathbf{I},$$

so $\mathbf{A}$ is orthogonal.

(b) $\mathbf{A}^{-1} = \mathbf{A}^T = \begin{pmatrix} \tfrac{2}{7} & -\tfrac{6}{7} & \tfrac{3}{7} \\ \tfrac{6}{7} & \tfrac{3}{7} & \tfrac{2}{7} \\ -\tfrac{3}{7} & \tfrac{2}{7} & \tfrac{6}{7} \end{pmatrix}.$

(c) We evaluate the determinant of $\mathbf{A}$:

$$\begin{vmatrix} \tfrac{2}{7} & \tfrac{6}{7} & -\tfrac{3}{7} \\ -\tfrac{6}{7} & \tfrac{3}{7} & \tfrac{2}{7} \\ \tfrac{3}{7} & \tfrac{2}{7} & \tfrac{6}{7} \end{vmatrix}$$

$$= \tfrac{2}{7} \begin{vmatrix} \tfrac{3}{7} & \tfrac{2}{7} \\ \tfrac{2}{7} & \tfrac{6}{7} \end{vmatrix} - \tfrac{6}{7} \begin{vmatrix} -\tfrac{6}{7} & \tfrac{2}{7} \\ \tfrac{3}{7} & \tfrac{6}{7} \end{vmatrix} - \tfrac{3}{7} \begin{vmatrix} -\tfrac{6}{7} & \tfrac{3}{7} \\ \tfrac{3}{7} & \tfrac{2}{7} \end{vmatrix}$$

$$= \tfrac{2}{7} \left(\tfrac{18}{49} - \tfrac{4}{49} \right) - \tfrac{6}{7} \left(-\tfrac{36}{49} - \tfrac{6}{49} \right) - \tfrac{3}{7} \left(-\tfrac{12}{49} - \tfrac{9}{49} \right)$$

$$= \tfrac{1}{343} (28 + 252 + 63) = \tfrac{343}{343} = 1.$$

Therefore $\mathbf{A}$ represents a rotation of $\mathbb{R}^3$.

4.1 (a) The ellipse with equation

$$\frac{x^2}{a^2} + \frac{y^2}{b^2} = 1$$

is written in matrix form as

$$\mathbf{x}^T \begin{pmatrix} 1/a^2 & 0 \\ 0 & 1/b^2 \end{pmatrix} \mathbf{x} + \begin{pmatrix} 0 & 0 \end{pmatrix} \mathbf{x} - 1 = 0.$$

(b) The hyperbola with equation

$$\frac{x^2}{a^2} - \frac{y^2}{b^2} = 1$$

is written in matrix form as

$$\mathbf{x}^T \begin{pmatrix} 1/a^2 & 0 \\ 0 & -1/b^2 \end{pmatrix} \mathbf{x} + \begin{pmatrix} 0 & 0 \end{pmatrix} \mathbf{x} - 1 = 0.$$

(c) The parabola with equation

$$y^2 = 4ax$$

is written in matrix form as

$$\mathbf{x}^T \begin{pmatrix} 0 & 0 \\ 0 & 1 \end{pmatrix} \mathbf{x} + \begin{pmatrix} -4a & 0 \end{pmatrix} \mathbf{x} + 0 = 0.$$

4.2 We use Strategy 4.1.

Introduce matrices. We have

$$\mathbf{A} = \begin{pmatrix} 1 & -2 \\ -2 & 4 \end{pmatrix} \quad \text{and} \quad \mathbf{J} = \begin{pmatrix} -6 \\ -8 \end{pmatrix}.$$

Align the axes. The characteristic equation of $\mathbf{A}$ is

$$\begin{vmatrix} 1 - \lambda & -2 \\ -2 & 4 - \lambda \end{vmatrix} = 0.$$

We expand this determinant and obtain

$$(1 - \lambda)(4 - \lambda) - 4 = 0,$$

which simplifies to

$$\lambda^2 - 5\lambda = \lambda(\lambda - 5) = 0.$$

The eigenvalues of $\mathbf{A}$ are 5 and 0.

The eigenvector equations are

$$\begin{cases} (1 - \lambda)x - 2y = 0, \\ -2x + (4 - \lambda)y = 0. \end{cases}$$

$\boxed{\lambda = 5}$ The eigenvector equations become

$$\begin{cases} -4x - 2y = 0, \\ -2x - y = 0. \end{cases}$$

These equations are equivalent to the single equation

$$2x + y = 0,$$

which implies that $y = -2x$. Thus the eigenvectors corresponding to $\lambda = 5$ are the non-zero vectors of the form $(k, -2k)$.

An eigenvector of unit length corresponding to $\lambda = 5$ is $\left(\tfrac{1}{\sqrt{5}}, -\tfrac{2}{\sqrt{5}} \right)$.

$\boxed{\lambda = 0}$ The eigenvector equations become

$$\begin{cases} x - 2y = 0, \\ -2x + 4y = 0. \end{cases}$$

These equations are equivalent to the single equation

$$x - 2y = 0,$$

which implies that $x = 2y$. Thus the eigenvectors corresponding to $\lambda = 0$ are the non-zero vectors of the form $(2k, k)$.

An eigenvector of unit length corresponding to $\lambda = 0$ is $\left(\tfrac{2}{\sqrt{5}}, \tfrac{1}{\sqrt{5}} \right)$.

An orthonormal eigenvector basis of $\mathbf{A}$ is therefore

$$E = \left\{ \left(\tfrac{1}{\sqrt{5}}, -\tfrac{2}{\sqrt{5}} \right), \left(\tfrac{2}{\sqrt{5}}, \tfrac{1}{\sqrt{5}} \right) \right\}.$$

We use the eigenvectors in E to form the columns of the transition matrix:

$$\mathbf{P} = \begin{pmatrix} \tfrac{1}{\sqrt{5}} & \tfrac{2}{\sqrt{5}} \\ -\tfrac{2}{\sqrt{5}} & \tfrac{1}{\sqrt{5}} \end{pmatrix}.$$

Now,
$$\mathbf{P}^T \mathbf{A} \mathbf{P} = \begin{pmatrix} 5 & 0 \\ 0 & 0 \end{pmatrix}$$
and
$$\begin{aligned} \begin{pmatrix} f & g \end{pmatrix} &= \begin{pmatrix} -6 & -8 \end{pmatrix} \begin{pmatrix} \frac{1}{\sqrt{5}} & \frac{2}{\sqrt{5}} \\ -\frac{2}{\sqrt{5}} & \frac{1}{\sqrt{5}} \end{pmatrix} \\ &= \begin{pmatrix} \frac{10}{\sqrt{5}} & -\frac{20}{\sqrt{5}} \end{pmatrix} \\ &= \begin{pmatrix} 2\sqrt{5} & -4\sqrt{5} \end{pmatrix}. \end{aligned}$$
The equation of the conic is now
$$5(x')^2 + 2\sqrt{5}x' - 4\sqrt{5}y' + 5 = 0.$$
Translate the origin. Completing the square in this equation, we obtain
$$5\left(x' + \frac{\sqrt{5}}{5}\right)^2 - 1 - 4\sqrt{5}y' + 5 = 0.$$
Simplifying this equation and substituting $x'' = x' + \frac{1}{\sqrt{5}}$ and $y'' = y' - \frac{1}{\sqrt{5}}$, we obtain
$$5(x'')^2 - 4\sqrt{5}y'' = 0.$$
The equation of the conic in standard form is
$$(x'')^2 = \frac{4}{\sqrt{5}}y''.$$
The conic is a parabola.

4.3 We use Strategy 4.1.

Introduce matrices. We have
$$\mathbf{A} = \begin{pmatrix} 9 & -2 \\ -2 & 6 \end{pmatrix} \quad \text{and} \quad \mathbf{J} = \begin{pmatrix} -10 \\ -20 \end{pmatrix}.$$
Align the axes. We have
$$\mathbf{P}^T \mathbf{A} \mathbf{P} = \begin{pmatrix} 10 & 0 \\ 0 & 5 \end{pmatrix},$$
where
$$\mathbf{P} = \begin{pmatrix} \frac{2}{\sqrt{5}} & \frac{1}{\sqrt{5}} \\ -\frac{1}{\sqrt{5}} & \frac{2}{\sqrt{5}} \end{pmatrix}.$$
So
$$\begin{aligned} \begin{pmatrix} f & g \end{pmatrix} &= \begin{pmatrix} -10 & -20 \end{pmatrix} \begin{pmatrix} \frac{2}{\sqrt{5}} & \frac{1}{\sqrt{5}} \\ -\frac{1}{\sqrt{5}} & \frac{2}{\sqrt{5}} \end{pmatrix} \\ &= \begin{pmatrix} 0 & -\frac{50}{\sqrt{5}} \end{pmatrix} \\ &= \begin{pmatrix} 0 & -10\sqrt{5} \end{pmatrix}. \end{aligned}$$
The equation of the conic is now
$$10(x')^2 + 5(y')^2 - 10\sqrt{5}y' - 5 = 0.$$
Dividing through by 5, we obtain
$$2(x')^2 + (y')^2 - 2\sqrt{5}y' - 1 = 0.$$
Translate the origin. Completing the square in this equation, we obtain
$$2(x')^2 + (y' - \sqrt{5})^2 - 5 - 1 = 0.$$
Simplifying this equation and substituting $x'' = x'$ and $y'' = y' - \sqrt{5}$, we obtain
$$2(x'')^2 + (y'')^2 - 6 = 0.$$
The equation of the conic in standard form is
$$\frac{(x'')^2}{3} + \frac{(y'')^2}{6} = 1.$$
The conic is an ellipse.

4.4 We use Strategy 4.2

Introduce matrices. We have
$$\mathbf{A} = \begin{pmatrix} 1 & 0 & 0 \\ 0 & 1 & 0 \\ 0 & 0 & 1 \end{pmatrix}, \quad \mathbf{J} = \begin{pmatrix} -2 \\ 4 \\ -6 \end{pmatrix}.$$
Align the axes. The matrix is already in diagonal form. (The axes of the quadric are parallel to the x-axis, y-axis and z-axis of $\mathbb{R}^3$.)

Translate the origin. Writing $x' = x$, $y' = y$ and $z' = z$, and completing the squares in the equation, we obtain
$$(x' - 1)^2 - 1 + (y' + 2)^2 - 4 + (z' - 3)^2 - 9 - 11$$
$$= 0.$$
Simplifying this equation and substituting $x'' = x' - 1$, $y'' = y' + 2$ and $z'' = z' - 3$, we obtain
$$(x'')^2 + (y'')^2 + (z'')^2 - 25 = 0.$$
The equation of the quadric in standard form is
$$\frac{(x'')^2}{25} + \frac{(y'')^2}{25} + \frac{(z'')^2}{25} = 1.$$
This is the equation of an ellipsoid. (This ellipsoid is a sphere.)

4.5 We use Strategy 4.2.

Introduce matrices. We have
$$\mathbf{A} = \begin{pmatrix} 4 & 2 & 0 \\ 2 & 3 & 2 \\ 0 & 2 & 2 \end{pmatrix}, \quad \mathbf{J} = \begin{pmatrix} 12 \\ 0 \\ 12 \end{pmatrix}.$$
Align the axes. On page 32 we found that
$$\mathbf{P}^T \mathbf{A} \mathbf{P} = \begin{pmatrix} 6 & 0 & 0 \\ 0 & 3 & 0 \\ 0 & 0 & 0 \end{pmatrix},$$
where
$$\mathbf{P} = \begin{pmatrix} \frac{2}{3} & -\frac{2}{3} & \frac{1}{3} \\ \frac{2}{3} & \frac{1}{3} & -\frac{2}{3} \\ \frac{1}{3} & \frac{2}{3} & \frac{2}{3} \end{pmatrix}.$$
So
$$\begin{aligned} \begin{pmatrix} f & g & h \end{pmatrix} &= \begin{pmatrix} 12 & 0 & 12 \end{pmatrix} \begin{pmatrix} \frac{2}{3} & -\frac{2}{3} & \frac{1}{3} \\ \frac{2}{3} & \frac{1}{3} & -\frac{2}{3} \\ \frac{1}{3} & \frac{2}{3} & \frac{2}{3} \end{pmatrix} \\ &= \begin{pmatrix} 12 & 0 & 12 \end{pmatrix}. \end{aligned}$$
The equation of the quadric is now
$$6(x')^2 + 3(y')^2 + 12x' + 12z' + 18 = 0.$$
Translate the origin. Completing the squares in this equation, we obtain
$$6(x' + 1)^2 - 6 + 3(y')^2 + 12z' + 18 = 0.$$
Simplifying this equation and substituting $x'' = x' + 1$, $y'' = y'$ and $z'' = z' + 1$, we obtain
$$2(x'')^2 + (y'')^2 + 4z'' = 0.$$
The equation of the quadric in standard form is
$$\frac{(x'')^2}{2} + \frac{(y'')^2}{4} = -z''.$$
This is the equation of an elliptic paraboloid.

There are many possible solutions to each of the remaining exercises in this section, representing different orderings of the eigenvectors.

4.6 We use Strategy 4.1.

Introduce matrices. We have
$$\mathbf{A} = \begin{pmatrix} 1 & 0 \\ 0 & -2 \end{pmatrix} \quad \text{and} \quad \mathbf{J} = \begin{pmatrix} -4 \\ -12 \end{pmatrix}.$$

Align the axes. The matrix is already in diagonal form. The axes of the conic are parallel to the x-axis and y-axis of $\mathbb{R}^2$.

Translate the origin. Completing the squares in the equation, we obtain
$$(x' - 2)^2 - 4 - 2(y' + 3)^2 + 18 - 18 = 0.$$

Simplifying this equation and substituting $x'' = x' - 2$ and $y'' = y' + 3$, we obtain
$$(x'')^2 - 2(y'')^2 - 4 = 0.$$

The equation of the conic in standard form is
$$\frac{(x'')^2}{4} - \frac{(y'')^2}{2} = 1.$$

The conic is a hyperbola.

4.7 We use Strategy 4.1.

Introduce matrices. We have
$$\mathbf{A} = \begin{pmatrix} 5 & -1 \\ -1 & 5 \end{pmatrix} \quad \text{and} \quad \mathbf{J} = \begin{pmatrix} 0 \\ 0 \end{pmatrix}.$$

Align the axes. In Exercise 3.7 you showed that
$$\mathbf{P}^T \mathbf{A} \mathbf{P} = \begin{pmatrix} 6 & 0 \\ 0 & 4 \end{pmatrix},$$

where
$$\mathbf{P} = \begin{pmatrix} \frac{1}{\sqrt{2}} & \frac{1}{\sqrt{2}} \\ -\frac{1}{\sqrt{2}} & \frac{1}{\sqrt{2}} \end{pmatrix}.$$

There are no linear x or y terms, so
$$\begin{pmatrix} f & g \end{pmatrix} = \begin{pmatrix} 0 & 0 \end{pmatrix}.$$

The equation of the conic is now
$$6(x')^2 + 4(y')^2 - 1 = 0.$$

Translate the origin. The conic is centred at the origin, since there are no linear x or y terms. No translation is required.

The equation of the conic in standard form is
$$6(x'')^2 + 4(y'')^2 = 1.$$

The conic is an ellipse.

4.8 We use Strategy 4.2.

Introduce matrices. We have
$$\mathbf{A} = \begin{pmatrix} 0 & 1 & 0 \\ 1 & 0 & 0 \\ 0 & 0 & 0 \end{pmatrix} \quad \text{and} \quad \mathbf{J} = \begin{pmatrix} -6 \\ 10 \\ 1 \end{pmatrix}.$$

Align the axes. In Exercise 3.8 you showed that
$$\mathbf{P}^T \mathbf{A} \mathbf{P} = \begin{pmatrix} 1 & 0 & 0 \\ 0 & 0 & 0 \\ 0 & 0 & -1 \end{pmatrix},$$

where
$$\mathbf{P} = \begin{pmatrix} \frac{1}{\sqrt{2}} & 0 & \frac{1}{\sqrt{2}} \\ \frac{1}{\sqrt{2}} & 0 & -\frac{1}{\sqrt{2}} \\ 0 & 1 & 0 \end{pmatrix}.$$

So
$$\begin{pmatrix} f & g & h \end{pmatrix} = \begin{pmatrix} -6 & 10 & 1 \end{pmatrix} \begin{pmatrix} \frac{1}{\sqrt{2}} & 0 & \frac{1}{\sqrt{2}} \\ \frac{1}{\sqrt{2}} & 0 & -\frac{1}{\sqrt{2}} \\ 0 & 1 & 0 \end{pmatrix}$$
$$= \begin{pmatrix} \frac{4}{\sqrt{2}} & 1 & -\frac{16}{\sqrt{2}} \end{pmatrix}$$
$$= \begin{pmatrix} 2\sqrt{2} & 1 & -8\sqrt{2} \end{pmatrix}.$$

The equation of the quadric is now
$$(x')^2 - (z')^2 + 2\sqrt{2}x' + y' - 8\sqrt{2}z' - 30 = 0.$$

Translate the origin. Completing the squares in this equation, we obtain
$$(x' + \sqrt{2})^2 - 2 + y' - (z' + 4\sqrt{2})^2 + 32 - 30 = 0.$$

Simplifying this equation and substituting $x'' = x' + \sqrt{2}$, $y'' = y'$ and $z'' = z' + 4\sqrt{2}$, we obtain
$$(x'')^2 + y'' - (z'')^2 = 0.$$

The equation of the quadric in standard form is
$$y'' = -(x'')^2 + (z'')^2.$$

This is the equation of a hyperbolic paraboloid.

4.9 We use Strategy 4.2.

Introduce matrices. We have
$$\mathbf{A} = \begin{pmatrix} 1 & 0 & 0 \\ 0 & 1 & 0 \\ 0 & 0 & 0 \end{pmatrix} \quad \text{and} \quad \mathbf{J} = \begin{pmatrix} 1 \\ 0 \\ -1 \end{pmatrix}.$$

Align the axes. The matrix is already in diagonal form. The axes of the quadric are parallel to the x-axis, y-axis and z-axis of $\mathbb{R}^3$.

Translate the origin. Completing the squares in the equation, we obtain
$$(x + \tfrac{1}{2})^2 - \tfrac{1}{4} + y^2 - z = 0.$$

Simplifying this equation and substituting $x' = x + \tfrac{1}{2}$, $y' = y$ and $z' = z + \tfrac{1}{4}$, we obtain
$$(x')^2 + (y')^2 - z' = 0.$$

The equation of the quadric in standard form is
$$z' = (x')^2 + (y')^2.$$

This is the equation of an elliptic paraboloid.

4.10 We use Strategy 4.2.

Introduce matrices. We have
$$\mathbf{A} = \begin{pmatrix} 0 & 1 & 0 \\ 1 & 0 & 0 \\ 0 & 0 & 0 \end{pmatrix} \quad \text{and} \quad \mathbf{J} = \begin{pmatrix} 0 \\ 0 \\ 1 \end{pmatrix}.$$

Align the axes. This matrix $\mathbf{A}$ is the same as the matrix $\mathbf{A}$ in Exercise 4.8, so we have

$$\mathbf{P}^T \mathbf{A} \mathbf{P} = \begin{pmatrix} 1 & 0 & 0 \\ 0 & 0 & 0 \\ 0 & 0 & -1 \end{pmatrix},$$

where

$$\mathbf{P} = \begin{pmatrix} \frac{1}{\sqrt{2}} & 0 & \frac{1}{\sqrt{2}} \\ \frac{1}{\sqrt{2}} & 0 & -\frac{1}{\sqrt{2}} \\ 0 & 1 & 0 \end{pmatrix}.$$

So

$$\begin{pmatrix} f & g & h \end{pmatrix} = \begin{pmatrix} 0 & 0 & 1 \end{pmatrix} \begin{pmatrix} \frac{1}{\sqrt{2}} & 0 & \frac{1}{\sqrt{2}} \\ \frac{1}{\sqrt{2}} & 0 & -\frac{1}{\sqrt{2}} \\ 0 & 1 & 0 \end{pmatrix}$$

$$= \begin{pmatrix} 0 & 1 & 0 \end{pmatrix}.$$

The equation of the quadric is now

$$(x')^2 - (z')^2 + y' = 0.$$

Translate the origin. The quadric is centred at the origin. No translation is required.

The equation of the quadric in standard form is

$$y' = -(x')^2 + (z')^2.$$

This is the equation of a hyperbolic paraboloid.

Index